CHILTON'S MODERN BOATING GUIDE SERIES

Under the Advisory Editorship of Hank Wieand Bowman

Care and Repair of Your Outboard Motor

HANK BOWMAN

CHILTON COMPANY — BOOK DIVISION

Publishers

Philadelphia   *New York*

Library of Congress Catalog Card No. 59-15041

Second Printing, January 1962

Contents

Introduction

The present-day outboard motor is no longer a cantanker-ous, noisy, smelly, and undependable piece of machinery. It is as little prone to mechanical failure as your automobile engine. But, like any piece of machinery, it requires maintenance. Without some effort on the part of its owner to care for it, ultimately any outboard motor will show the results of abuse, fail to function efficiently, stop operating entirely, or fail to start.

Incorporated in the contemporary outboard power plant are numerous refinements that offer the operator greater ease, safety, and comfort. Full forward-neutral-reverse gearshifts or completely reversing power plants of the forward-stop-restart-reverse type are commonplace, as are remote steering, with combined remote shift, throttle, and magneto controls.

The majority of the larger horsepower motors sold are equipped with turn-key or push-button electric starting. Many of these motors also feature generators. Tremendous advances have been made in silencing. Powerheads are no longer ex-posed and gasoline-oil fuel supplies have been taken off the tops of the motors and are contained in convenient carry-aboard tanks. Ignition systems have been improved, car-buretion refined, and even the metal alloys are better in many ways than those used in the past: lighter in weight but stronger and more resistant to corrosion.

With all of these refinements the outboard motor has become a smoother functioning, more powerful, dependable, and highly efficient boat propulsion unit, but the changes have also brought with them one drawback. There was a time not many years ago when any reasonably talented home hobby mechanic could disassemble and reassemble his outboard motor with a minimum of tools—a crescent wrench, pliers, and blade screw-driver. With no complex starting features, the simplest (though not overly efficient) ignition and carburetion system, no shift-ing mechanisms to complicate the lower end, no remote con-trols to do likewise with the top side, repairs were simple.

Closer tolerances for smoother running and longer wear, im-proved induction valving, needle, roller and ball bearings re-placing bronze bushings, the addition of water pumps, even thermostats, and rewind starters have made the outboard motor too complex for full repairs by other than specially trained mechanics. Numerous special tools are needed for any major overhaul and these are different for every make engine.

This drawback, too, is true of the automobile engine. Few car owners today make any attempt to handle all repairs and replacements themselves. However, an engine failure in an automobile seldom puts its owner in danger. He can walk to the nearest telephone and call for help.

An outboard motor failure may occur far from shore. It can happen in a strong current that could sweep your boat and its occupants into a hazardous position. Swimming for help isn't as simple as walking or hitchhiking.

Because of this greater need for complete efficiency of an outboard motor, every outboard motor operator should understand the basics of two-cycle power plant operation. The important maintenance items should be carefully checked and taken care of at regular intervals.

Though few outboard operators have any desire to become skilled mechanics capable of repairing any make and model outboard engine, every outboard operator should be able to spot the development of potential troubles. Most outboard motor failures could be avoided if the telltale signs of trouble were spotted in advance by their owners.

With a knowledge of troubleshooting, an outboard motor owner can have minor mechanical ailments remedied before major problems develop.

Well-maintained outboard motors do not fail. One major outboard manufacturer operated a pair of motors, with routine maintenance only, for 50,000 miles, the equivalent of two circuits of the earth at the equator, with no mechanical failure. Another manufacturer sponsored a successful cross-Atlantic voyage with outboard power.

With a knowledge of outboard motor maintenance, you need not contemplate an ocean crossing or a trip around the world to put this information to use. But it should aid in making your everyday outboard motorboating wholly pleasurable and uninterrupted by the frustration accompanying breakdowns.

1. How the Outboard Motor Works

Just as there is more than a hint of truth in the stadium hawker's cry, "You can't follow the game without a program," so it is difficult to maintain an outboard motor without having a basic idea of its principle of operation.

The outboard engine is a piston-driven gasoline engine of the two-cycle or two-stroke cycle type as differentiated from the commonplace automobile engine which operates on a four-cycle principle. The two-cycle outboard motor in many respects is more efficient than the four-cycle of comparable piston displacement. Light weight per horsepower developed and a high horsepower to cubic inch piston displacement are among the two-cycle engine's most favorable attributes.

The basic difference between the two- and four-cycle engines lies in the power impulse sequence. In a four-cycle engine, each cylinder fires every other time its piston reaches the top of its travel, or moves the greatest distance from the crankshaft to which it is connected. Each cylinder of a two-cycle engine, by contrast, produces a power impulse, that is fuel is ignited and expanding gases exert a thrust on the crown of the piston, every time the two-cycle's piston reaches the extreme of its travel.

Expressed in a somewhat different way, each piston in an automobile four-cycle engine moves up and down inside a given cylinder alternately under power of combustion during one rotation of the crankshaft and without combustion on the next crankshaft rotation. The two-cycle, by contrast, produces a working combustion impulse for each in-and-out movement of a piston.

The reason for the variance in names of the two designs then becomes apparent. The two-stroke or two-cycle produces power during every rotation of the crankshaft, with the piston making an in-and-out thrust or two strokes. The four-cycle produces its power every other revolution of the crankshaft, the piston stroking in-out-in-out, four strokes per power impulse. As a result of this variance of power impulses, if engines of the two different designs are fitted with cylinders of identical bores, piston size, connecting rods and crankshaft, the two-cycle may be expected to produce twice as much power since each piston produces twice as many power strokes. In actual practice, this doesn't quite occur since the two types of power

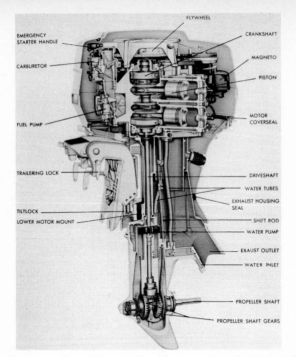

Cutaway view of an outboard motor showing internal arrangements of vital parts common to most two-cycle engines. (Courtesy, Johnson Motors)

plants vary in their means of introducing and expelling or scavenging fuel vapor and burned or partially burned gases.

The four-cycle engine is fitted with individual fuel-vapor intake and exhaust gas valves for each cylinder. Though the mechanical means utilized to operate the four-cycle valving system adds to the manufacturing complications of the design, resulting in added weight, cost, and more parts to wear and maintain, the four-cycle power plant does make a more efficient use of fuel and converts a greater percentage of fuel used to power.

In the two-cycle engine the piston serves as both inlet and exhaust valve.

The top of each two-cycle piston is designed with a deflector on the crown of the piston as can be noted in the diagram. As the piston moves downward on its power stroke, the downward movement of the piston reduces the volume of the crankcase, and fuel vapor induced into the crankcase is compressed. As the piston continues its stroke toward the crankcase, it slides past intake holes or ports in the cylinder wall. Thus as the piston slides clear of the holes, the piston performs the same function as a four-cycle's valve opening. Vaporized fuel in the crankcase rushes under pressure through these holes. Slightly before the intake port is uncovered, another set of holes, the exhaust ports, are uncovered by the travel of the piston, and the exhaust gases under pressure seek to escape and rush out under pressure through the exhaust ports. So, nearly simultaneously, the burned gases are scavenged from the cylinder and a fresh charge of vaporized fuel is introduced. As the piston moves upward again, the exhaust ports and the intake ports are closed by the piston sliding past, and the fresh fuel vapor that has entered the cylinder is compressed.

Shortly before the piston reaches top dead center, a spark is produced by the spark plug and the compressed fuel vapor is set afire. The rapid expansion of burning gases forces the piston downward and the whole sequence is repeated.

The motion of the piston, connecting rod, and crankshaft has been compared to the operation of a brace and bit when drilling a hole. You will recall that one hand grasps a stationary pad at the top of the brace. This pad could be likened to the top of the crankcase. The person operating the brace grips a handle that is mounted eccentrically on the brace. The arm and elbow are then moved back and forth in a reciprocating motion to cause the bit to revolve. The forearm corresponds to the connecting rod, with the handgrip operating in a manner similar to a crankshaft throw. The elbow simulates piston movement, and this thrusting motion is translated into the rotating motion of the bit which corresponds to the rotating crankshaft.

The movement of the piston also produces another action. As the piston moves upward or outward on a compression stroke, a low pressure or partial vacuum is created in the crankcase. This unseats a reed- or butterfly-type valve in the crankcase or manifold which sucks an air-fuel mixture from the carburetor. When the piston starts its downward stroke again, and the gases in the crankcase are compressed, the reed- or butterfly-type valving is forced under pressure to reseat or close over the intake port or ports. These valves, small spring leafs of steel or beryllium-copper, or other metal alloys compounded to resist fatigue, vary somewhat in their degree of

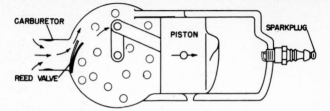

Illustrating induction of gasoline-oil-air mixture into crankcase as piston moves upward toward compression.

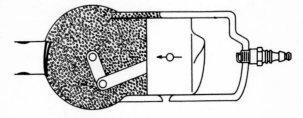

As piston moves downward, reed valve assembly is closed and fuel is compressed within crankcase.

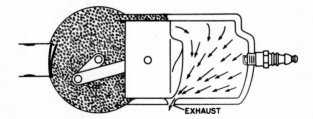

As piston moves farther downward, exhaust port is opened and burned gases begin to escape.

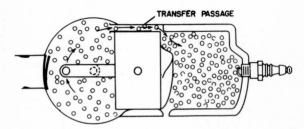

Here piston has reached bottom of its stroke, and both exhaust and fuel intake ports are open. Compressed fuel in crankcase rushes into combustion chamber.

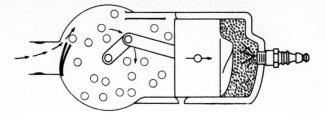

As piston moves upward again, completing its two strokes, the fuel-air mixture, fully compressed, is set on fire by spark plug. Expansion of the burning gases will start piston downward again.
(Courtesy, Scott Motors)

opening. As engine speeds increase, crankcase pressure varies, causing an automatic metering of amounts of fuel induced into the cylinders.

You will see from this that the two-cycle offers the advantage of having fewer parts than the four-cycle, and also does not waste horsepower in providing some means to motivate mechanical intake and exhaust valves. This simplification of design is the feature that permits high efficiency with low weight, and an elimination of much of the mechanical complexity inherent in the four-cycle engine.

Another basic difference exists, representing an additional simplification favoring the two-cycle. This concerns the lubrication system. With the two-cycle, the engine lubricant required to reduce friction of rotating and reciprocating parts is provided very simply by mixing oil with the gasoline. During the course of each two strokes or cycles, all internal parts of the two-cycle engine are bathed with oil. The four-cycle engine must be provided with some mechanical means to supply lubrication to rotating and reciprocating parts since the four-cycle design does not call for oil to be mixed with the fuel. Rather, the lubricant is supplied from an oil storage sump in the crankcase. Distribution of oil to the engine is accomplished either with a splash, pressure, or combination splash-pressure system in which the movement of the crank and crank throws splash lubricant over the four-cycle's moving parts, or oil is pumped by mechanical means to parts to be lubricated.

Fuel for the two-cycle is more expensive since, unlike the four-cycle, the oil mixed into the gasoline-oil fuel mixture is constantly consumed. The four-cycle power plant reuses its lubricant with only a small amount of the oil being burned

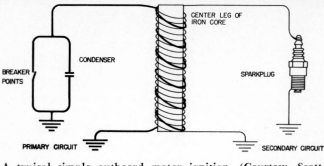

A typical simple outboard motor ignition. (Courtesy, Scott Motors)

in the ignition process. While the latter is an economy, the lubricant of the four-cycle quickly becomes laden with dirt, gum, tar, and other foreign materials as well as being diluted by gasoline vapors passing down the cylinder walls into the crankcase. Hence more rapid wear can be expected to occur in the four-cycle than in the two-cycle power plant. Should any of the oil-circulating passages of a four-cycle lubricating system clog, certain parts will be cut off from lubrication and will be damaged or destroyed. Though somewhat wasteful of lubricant, the two-cycle method of lubrication is far more positive. All that is required of a two-cycle outboard to be assured of ample lubrication is oil of the recommended type and proportions properly mixed with the gasoline.

The inherent inefficiency of fuel consumption in the two-cycle is caused by a fresh fuel charge entering the cylinder while the exhaust port of that cylinder is still open. The deflector on the crown of the piston is designed to prevent the fresh fuel vapor from moving directly across the cylinder and out through the open exhaust port. Despite this piston deflector, some of the fresh charge does escape out of the exhaust port on each stroke. The four-cycle valving system, by contrast, traps all fuel vapor induced into the cylinder and does not waste part of it by permitting it to pass unconsumed out the exhaust passages.

On the ordinary two-cylinder, alternate-firing outboard motor, one cylinder delivers a power stroke as the other moves up on a fuel induction-compression stroke. Thus on every 180-degree rotation of the crankshaft, a power impulse occurs.

The two alternately firing pistons offset one another so that the operation of the modern outboard motor is smoother than with single-cylinder outboard motors or outboard motors of the older opposed-firing type in which both cylinders fire simultaneously.

Even greater smoothness is realized with engines of three-, four-, and six-cylinder design since these cylinders, too, fire at equally timed intervals of crankshaft rotation with a proportionately lesser interval between each power impulse.

As already mentioned, lubrication in the two-cycle engine is provided by mixing oil with gasoline. Since oil is less volatile than gasoline, a large portion of the lubricant drops out of suspension in the fuel-air vapor induced into the engine. This oil mist clings to bearings and other moving parts in the crankcase. Those amounts of oil remaining in suspension in the vaporized fuel enter the cylinder, aid in providing a seal between the pistons and the cylinder wall, and at the same time provide lubrication to the piston, the piston rings, cylinder walls, and the connecting rods and bearings. Because of this it cannot be stressed too much or too frequently that every outboarder should very carefully mix with his gasoline the amount of lubricant specified by the manufacturer, and mix the two thoroughly.

An outboard engine in addition to having a means to compress fuel, requires a metering system to supply fuel to the cylinders and some means to ignite the fuel. If all three of these fundamentals, fuel, compression, and spark, are present and in proper functioning condition, the engine will run.

A carburetor serves as a means for mixing fuel with air and for metering this air-fuel vapor to the cylinders in proper quantities.

Keep in mind that an engine burns air as well as gasoline. In fact, it will burn far more air than gasoline—approximately one part of gasoline to eight to fifteen parts of air. Maintaining the proper proportion of air to gasoline has a considerable effect on an engine's performance.

The spark to ignite the compressed air-fuel vapor is most commonly provided by a magneto, though some outboard engines are fitted with automotive-type distributors and a battery ignition.

Cooling for the outboard motor, with a few exceptions in the most modest-sized units, is provided by circulating water in jackets around the cylinder and the exhaust passages.

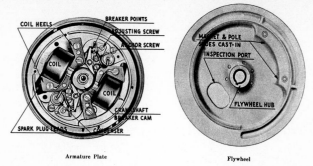

Various components of a flywheel-type magneto used on a two-cylinder outboard motor. (Courtesy, Johnson Motors)

The outboard engine basically is divided into two sections: the powerhead which produces the rotating movement of the crankshaft and the lower unit which translates the rotating movement of the crankshaft via a drive shaft and gears to the propeller shaft and ultimately to the propeller located on the trailing end of the lower unit gear case.

Most current models of outboards are fitted with a forward-neutral-reverse full gearshift.

A variance in full shift is found in several of the larger models of Mercury motors. These are equipped with completely reversing power; i.e., crankshaft and flywheel may be operated in both clockwise and counterclockwise directions. Thus such engines may be started in either forward or reverse. There is no neutral. To change direction, a single lever is pulled to a midpoint in the shift range, the motor stops, and a button on top of the shifting lever is depressed as the motor is put into the desired direction of movement, forward or reverse.

The lower unit gearing in this type of motor operation is simplified since the gears of the propeller shaft and those of the drive shaft are in constant contact.

The more conventional type of gearshift outboard motor is equipped with a neutral; the engine can be in operation without the propeller turning. The gearbox is fitted with what is termed a dog clutch. The gear attached to the bottom of the drive shaft, which rotates at the same speed and as an extension of the engine's crankshaft, may be alternately meshed with a set of gears forward of it or behind it. If the forward set

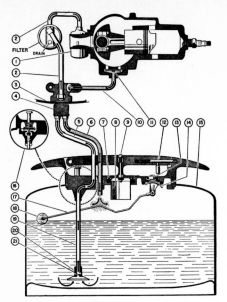

Pressure Fuel System

1 Carburetor
2 Fuel line, filter to carburetor
3 Bottom cowl
4 Twist connector
5 Fuel line, tank to twist connector
6 Air line, tank to twist connector
7 Seal
8 Extension tube, filler opening
9 Pressure relief valve
10 Air line, crankcase to connector
11 Pressurized valve, crankcase
12 Release latch
13 Magnifying lens
14 Graduated sector
15 Remote fuel tank
16 Priming pump
17 Float arm
18 Float
19 Fuel pick-up tube
20 Disc filter
21 Check valve

An outboard motor pressure fuel system with various key components identified. (Courtesy, Mercury Motors)

of propeller shaft gears is intermeshed with the drive-shaft gears, the propeller shaft will operate in one direction. If the two gears on the propeller shaft are moved by a forklike lever so that neither set of gears is in contact with the drive-shaft gear, the propeller shaft does not turn and the motor is in neutral. If the trailing gear of the two on the propeller shaft is meshed with the drive-shaft gear, the direction of propeller rotation is reversed.

Aside from these two major sections of the outboard motor, several other component parts are required. One of these is the means to secure the entire power package to the transom of

THERMOSTATIC CONTROLLED
COOLING SYSTEM

Diagram labels: CYLINDER HEAD, CYLINDER, PRESSURE CONTROL VALVE, THERMOSTAT TO OPEN AT 150°, WATER PUMP, EXHAUST TUBE COOLING, OUTLET FOR WATER OVER 150°, WATER 150° F. OR LESS GOES BACK THRU PUMP, WATER INTAKE (COLD)

**Most outboard motors are water cooled. Illustrating
use of a thermostat in a four-cylinder Evinrude
outboard motor.**

the boat. This is done by a mounting bracket fitted with a
set of thumbscrew clamps. As an added attraction to the de-
tachable-type motor, all present outboard motors are fitted
with a tilt-up feature—that is, the motor can pivot at the motor
bracket mounting location should the motor strike a submerged object or when the boat is driven into shallow water
for beaching.

As a convenience, the outboard motor in all but the smallest
units is fitted with a remote from the powerhead fuel supply.
The fuel systems vary. Many of the older ones were pressurized. Newer outboard motors are equipped with a far safer
nonpressurized fuel system, and the powerhead is fitted with
a fuel pump to provide a constant supply of fuel to the carburetor. Both the pressurized and the nonpressurized remote
tanks may be uncoupled quickly when the fuel is used up, and
a spare filled tank coupled into position so that outboarders
cruising beyond the range of a single tank may switch tanks
without the engine even coming to a stop.

2. Proper Break-in Important

When you buy an outboard motor, you're buying fun. You may think that just because you put your money on the line, from then on it's up to the motor to make you have a good time.

Actually fun with your outboard motor is not much different from marriage. There's got to be a bit of give and take on both sides, particularly at the start.

Every major outboard manufacturer runs each motor in a test tank before it is released and sent to a dealer. This means your brand-new motor has been run, but it hasn't really been broken in because it hasn't been operated under load—that is pushing a boat and passengers.

Impatient as doubtless you will be to see what performance your new motor will offer, you should take a number of basic precautions before getting underway for the first time.

Before you launch your boat, check the lower unit lubricant. The cigar-shaped section just forward of the propeller contains the propeller gears and in many installations the dog clutch shift mechanism. The moving parts in the gear case must be protected from rust, corrosion, and wear. Though gear cases usually are filled at the factory before the motors

Prior to running any outboard motor, check lower unit lubricant to be certain that gear case housing has ample lubrication. Be sure to fill it with type of lubricant specified. Some, such as this, require hypoid oil.

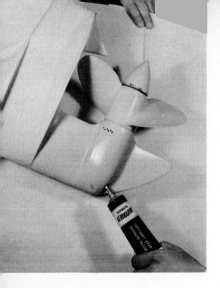

Other units call for lower unit grease.

are shipped or by dealers before sale to the customer, this is not always the case. A few hours' operation without adequate lubrication can play havoc with the innards of the gearbox.

Be certain to use the prescribed type of lubricant. Some lower units are designed for lubrication with a hypoid oil; others call for waterproof grease. The two lubricants never should be mixed, and the wrong kind should not be used.

Let's not lose the motor overboard before you've had a chance to get to know it. Many of the newer, larger horse-power outboard motors require bolting as well as clamping to the transom. If yours is one of these, and the manufacturer's manual of instructions will mention this if it is, be certain that the motor is not only thumbscrewed tightly to the transom but that bolts are placed through the slots provided in the clamp brackets and are bolted completely through the transom. If you do this, your new motor can't jump overboard in its first turn.

If the motor is not provided with some means for bolting, then I recommend that you tie or chain the motor to the boat. You may have to install a large eye bolt through the transom so that you have something to tie to.

The transom motor-mounting cutout heights of outboard boats vary from 15″ to 20″ or more. Motors with standard lower units usually call for a transom height of 15″ to 17″, extra length units for heights of 20″ and upward. While the transom height will be particularly important to you when you are later setting up your motor for maximum performance, it is vital during the break-in period that the motor not be mounted too high. If your motor is designed for operation, for example, on a 15″ transom, placing the motor on a 17″ transom will allow the propeller to rev up excessively, which will be particularly bad for the new, stiff engine.

Though some manufacturers state that their motors need no break-in, their maintenance manuals usually suggest that the buyer of one of their new motors operate it with care and avoid sustained high speed during the first hours of operation. If this sounds like so much double talk to you, frankly it does to me, too. All of the internal rolling, sliding parts of any new motor, no matter how carefully those parts have been machined and fitted, will require a bit of mating and wearing down of the high spots before the motor can be expected to operate smoothly. A brief factory run-in will not accomplish this, but rather merely will establish that the motor will start readily and operate adequately.

The first few tankloads of fuel that you will run through

Care should be taken to mix gasoline and oil to manufacturer's specifications. Make it a practice to screen all fuel to remove any foreign matter.

your motor may well be the most important gulps of gas and oil the motor will ever get. Start out by mixing your fuel carefully. Don't guess. Measure the proportions of oil to gas. There is no standardization of lubrication for two-cycle motors. This is due in part to a variance of opinion among the engineers of rival manufacturers. It also is dictated by the internal design of the motor itself, tolerances between sliding and rotating parts, design of bearings, seals, and other mechanical features. Because variances in design do exist, follow the manufacturer's recommendations for your particular model of motor. This is important, for prescribed quantities of oil may not even be the same for every model made by an individual manufacturer.

Use a consistent method of mixing oil to gasoline each time you prepare your fuel. First add a small amount of gasoline to your fuel can or remote fuel tank. Then pour in the required quantity of oil for the total amount of gasoline you plan to use. Shake this mixture well. Then add the balance of the gasoline and mix again.

A few grains of sand or tiny amount of any foreign material in your fuel mixture can cause carburetion problems. Your motor probably will be fitted with a sediment bowl for the carburetor. This is intended to collect foreign matter that may

Before getting underway with a new outfit, be certain that steering cables are properly adjusted and fastenings are secure.

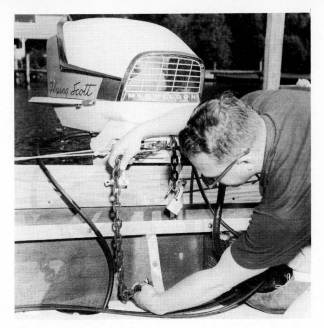

If provisions are made for bolting on your motor, *do so!* Some outboarders take the precaution of chaining or tying motor to boat's transom. A padlock added to chain will offset chance of theft.

have worked into the fuel supply system. Proper precautions taken during the fuel mixing process will prevent the need for frequent cleaning of the fuel sediment bowl. Do not put the hose nozzle directly into your remote fuel tanks; instead flow the gasoline through a funnel equipped with a fine mesh screen. This will trap any water, gum, varnish, or dirt.

During the first two tankloads of gasoline run through your motor, I recommend adding 50 per cent more than the factory-recommended quantity of lubricant in your fuel-oil formula. For example, if the operating manual calls for a half pint of lubricant to a gallon of gasoline, during the first two tankloads I would suggest the use of three-quarters of a pint to a gallon.

This excess of oil will cause your engine to smoke a bit and it may even result in fouling the spark plugs with a quick accumulation of carbon, but it will assure ample lube to the moving parts. Because of this, I recommend, too, that you re-move the spark plugs after two tankloads of fuel have been run through the motor, clean the plugs with a toothbrush and a solvent solution, regap the electrodes, and then replace them.

During the break-in period, operate the motor largely in the half- to three-quarter throttle range. Occasionally during the break-in, vary the motor's speed by squeezing the throttle, then slowing almost immediately to cruising speed again. These periodic bursts of full throttle will give the motor's insides added doses of a richer fuel mixture, bathing the internal parts with generous quantities of lubricant.

During the break-in period, don't overwork the motor by turning tightly and forcing the engine to labor, and don't pull water skiers or carry large passenger loads. While the motor is still stiff, let it work no harder than is necessary.

Think of your motor as an athlete capable of a topflight performance, but one who must warm up slowly so as not to strain muscles and ligaments until they have had a chance to become limber.

After the shakedown period, during which your new motor will have consumed a minimum of two full tankloads of fuel, give the motor a check-over. Remove the motor's cowling. Inspect all securing bolts and screws. Some of them will have loosened during the break-in, or some may not have been tightly secured during the factory assembly process. Check the lower unit lube again. It's a good idea to flush the grease out of the unit and replace it with wholly fresh lubricant. You can flush it by using a squirt-type oil can fitted with a nozzle and loaded with your regular gasoline-oil fuel mixture, kerosene, or a commercial grease solvent. This flushing will wash away any tiny particles of metal which chipped from the gear teeth during the gear-mating period, and it will pre-vent these metal chips from ultimately working into and caus-ing lower unit bearings to wear rapidly.

As the motor loosens and gradually becomes freer, the car-buretor settings require change. You will find that the motor will operate smoothly on a leaner fuel mixture after the break-in period. It will also idle more smoothly and effortlessly, so that the low speed or idling jet should also be adjusted once the break-in period has been completed.

The break-in is the shakedown period. Expect a few items to vibrate and work loose. This is natural and just as the new automobile is usually returned to the dealer for a 1,000-mile check-up, so most marine dealers will offer you a 5- or 10-hour check-up service for the new outboard motor.

At the same time the motor is being inspected for loose securing hardware, it is well to go over the boat's steering and inspect the remote controls. These, too, will have been new, and, during the shakedown, pulley sheave and steering wheel securing bolts, remove throttle and shift control brackets, and other parts making up the control linkage also may have loosened.

3. Routine Maintenance

One especially nice thing about the two-cycle outboard motor is that you never have to have the crankcase oil changed. However, a regular over-all motor maintenance program should be followed out just as it is with the automobile.

Since many boatmen operate their outboard equipment in salt water or in water contaminated by industrial by-products, and since motors are frequently left on boats moored in the water, owners should safeguard the exposed motor parts against corrosive effects.

One of the best practices, of course, is to remove the motor from the boat immediately after any salt-water operation. Then the exterior parts of the lower unit should be flushed with fresh water, the motor should be wiped dry, and then wiped again with an oily cloth to coat exposed surfaces with a light protective film.

However, few owners of large-size power plants have the facilities available to lift the motor from the boat, and with remote controls attached and motors bolted, it is the rare boat-man who wants to bother to take the motor from his boat.

For on-the-water storage, tilt the lower unit and lock it upward in a tilted condition so that all of the underwater parts are free of the water. However, care should be taken not to tilt the motor in such a fashion that the lower unit is at a higher elevation than the powerhead, for this can cause any residue of cooling water remaining in the exhaust system to flow back into the cylinders through the exhaust ports, causing serious damage.

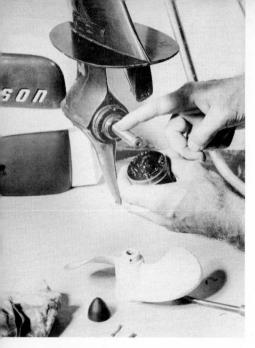

Whenever you remove propeller, coat its shaft with a film of waterproof grease to prevent propeller from corroding fast to shaft.

If you carry your outboard motor in the trunk or back of your car, stow it with powerhead slightly higher than the lower unit so that cooling system water cannot work its way into powerhead. (Courtesy, Gale Products)

Periodically remove spark plugs, clean and regap. Tighten all bolts.
(Courtesy, Evinrude Motors)

If your motor does not have a positive tilt-locking device, then it's recommended that you carry a block of wood that can be wedged between the clamp brackets and the drive-shaft housing to maintain the motor in a tilted position.

The protective cowling of most contemporary motors will prevent spray or rain from wetting any of the powerhead components. However, it's well periodically to remove the motor cowling, and wipe the ignition leads and spark plug insulators (that is the porcelain sections) in order to remove any dampness or collection of fuel that may have gathered on them and which could lead to shorting out.

Every twenty hours of operation it is a good idea to remove the spark plugs for inspection even though you have had no starting or operating difficulties. Remember that adequate maintenance makes repairs unnecessary. Clean the plugs if necessary and replace them once a season as a precaution. The condition of spark plugs is frequently indicative of the operating condition of your motor.

Inspect the high-tension ignition leads (spark plug wires) for any sign of damage or deterioration. Pay particular atten-

Set spark plug gaps with a special plug gapping tool; obtain from any marine dealer. (Courtesy, Evinrude Motors)

Check throttle and other linkages for worn or loose connections, then give a generous coating of a good waterproof lubricant. (Courtesy, Evinrude Motors)

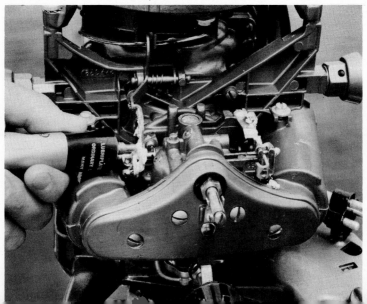

tion to those sections of insulation that may come in contact with metal parts of the motor. Vibration may have worn away the protective covering.

Remove the fuel filter and clean it.

Lubricate the swivel bracket and all remote-control junctions.

Inspect the fuel lines, both those remote from the motor and those under the cowling. Check for leakage and any evidence of damage or deterioration. Tighten all retaining hardware.

Inspect the propeller for damage. Minor nicks and burrs should be filed and the edges of the blades smoothed. Remove as little metal as possible, for this will throw the propeller out of balance and lead to vibration.

Remove the propeller and coat the propeller shaft with a waterproof grease. Lower unit lubricant is ideal. This will prevent the propeller hub and shaft from corroding and causing the propeller hub to seize permanently to the propeller shaft.

If your motor is of a type requiring a shear pin, inspect the shear pin for damage. It is a good idea to replace the shear pin, throwing the old one away, for the pin may have been strained without actually shearing.

Inspect all exposed metal surfaces for chips and scratches, for at these points rust or corrosion will start. All marine dealers carry handy-to-use cans of pressurized spray paint of colors to match cowlings or lower units of all popular-make motors. It is particularly important that any underwater areas from which paint has been removed be retouched. This isn't just for appearance, though that's important, too.

Many outboard motors are equipped with flushing attachments to which a garden hose may be fitted. If your motor has this feature, flush the cooling system regularly with fresh water as this will prevent the accumulation of scale that ultimately can clog your motor's cooling system. Owners of motors not so equipped should operate their motors in water tanks or barrels to flush the cooling system.

If you store your motor on the transom of the boat on a trailer during off-operating periods, with a little ingenuity you can rig a barrel in such a manner that you can back your trailer to it with the motor tilted up, then tilt the motor down so the lower unit is submerged, and operate the motor for a few minutes at idling speed, just long enough to pump fresh water through the system.

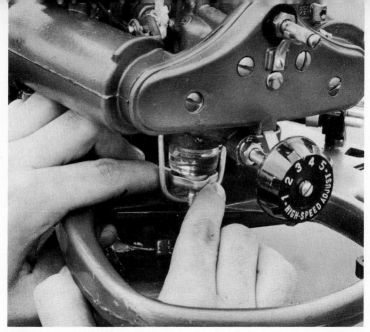

The carburetor sediment bowl keeps sludge and foreign matter from reaching carburetor. It is easy to remove—clean it at regular intervals. (Courtesy, Evinrude Motors)

If your motor is left clamped on the boat for over-the-road trailing, chock it at an angle with a block of wood or use a special lower unit support. (Courtesy, Scott Motors)

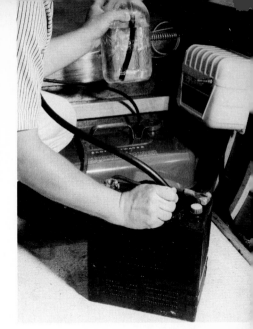

Check electrolyte level of your battery each time you use your boat. Add distilled water to keep plates covered ⅛″ to ¼″.

Since gums and fuel sediment can collect readily in carburetor bowls if they are left filled, after each period of operation, prior to covering the boat and motor at on-the-water moorings or reloading your outfit onto your trailer, disconnect fuel lines and allow the motor to idle until the fuel in the carburetor bowl has been exhausted and the carburetor has been run dry.

Do not leave partially filled fuel tanks in your boat. Condensation occurs in them readily, and ultimately considerable water will collect with the fuel. It is better to remove fuel tanks from your boat, drain them, and store remote tanks with the air bleed open. Or, refill them so they are ready for your next operation.

Many boatmen keep a gasoline-oil fuel storage drum and use their leftover outboard fuel in two-cycle lawn mowers.

Lead acid storage batteries used for electric-starting systems inherently have self-discharge characteristics. Storage batteries should be recharged every sixty days or whenever a specific gravity reading drops below 1.150. Distilled water should be added to the cells so that the plates of the battery are constantly kept covered to a depth of approximately ⅛″ to ¼″. Terminals of the battery should be kept free of corrosion and coated with petroleum jelly or a waterproof grease. Protect the storage battery from direct exposure to sun rays. If the motor is going to be stored for a long period, the battery should be removed from the boat and kept in a cool dry location.

Recharging a battery should be done at a rate of from four to no more than six amperes. "Quick charges" will shorten battery life.

4. Fuel System Maintenance and Troubleshooting

Unlike working a complicated jigsaw puzzle, one can be logical and systematic about locating the cause of starting failure or rough operating characteristics of a two-cycle engine. It is simplest to separate troubleshooting into three classifications: failures or faults attributable to the fuel supply system, the ignition system, or internal powerhead components.

The following is a troubleshooting list of the fuel system:
Check carburetor for fuel in the bowl.

If no fuel is reaching the carburetor:

Possible Causes:

1. Empty gas tank.
2. Fuel lines improperly connected or not connected.
3. Closed vent in gas tank.
4. Restricted or clogged vent in gas tank.
5. Fuel line shutoff valve closed.
6. Pinched or restricted fuel lines.
7. Failure to squeeze fuel-priming bulb.
8. No pressure in remote fuel tank.
9. Air leak in fuel tank pressure line.
10. Fuel pump failure.
11. Clogged filter at carburetor location or on fuel line between tank and carburetor.
12. Clogged filter in remote fuel tank.
13. Clogged carburetor screen.
14. High-speed metering valve closed.

REMEDIES:

1. In eliminating possible causes for fuel not reaching the carburetor, the first and most obvious item to be checked is fuel supply. If your tank is empty, you can put away your troubleshooting list, buy some fuel, or hoist a distress signal.

2. If there is fuel in your tank, the next most obvious possible failure will be due to improperly connected fuel line leads or fuel lines not connected at all. Plug the line in fully, for you must have a positive connection before you can expect a fuel flow.

3. If your motor is of relatively recent vintage, it will be fitted with a nonpressurized fuel system. The vent on the top of the remote fuel tank must be open. Air must go in for liquid to come out.

4. Not as obvious as the closed vent is the restricted vent. Dirt may have accumulated, causing a full or partial restriction of air flow. Screwing the vent valve all the way in and out several times will usually clear it of any restriction. Clothing or miscellaneous accessory gear may be piled over the vent.

5. Some motors are equipped with a fuel shutoff valve. This is commonplace to permanent tank installations in larger outboards. Be sure the valve is open.

6. Many outboarders are a bit casual about stowage of accessory gear. Better check to be sure an anchor or your ice chest isn't sitting on the flexible fuel line and cutting off or restricting the fuel flow.

7. Nonpressurized fuel systems often are fitted with a priming bulb. If yours has one, squeeze it rhythmically until the flexible bulb resists finger pressure. If the bulb gets hard, you know you are getting fuel at least that far.

If the fuel still fails to reach the carburetor, then check the fuel lines from the bulb forward for restrictions. The most logical spot for trouble would be at the connector assembly. Check at this point to be sure the ball-check spring valve is free to unseat.

Usually connectors are inserted in one of two ways: either with a straight thrust onto one or more prongs which unseat the check valve and provide a positive lock by means of a thumb-operated spring clip, or by inserting the fitting and giving it a half twist. The latter type also is provided with a positive lock in slotted retainers.

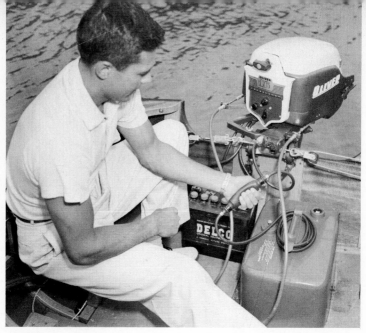

Nonpressurized fuel systems require that the fuel-priming bulb be squeezed before starting engine. (Courtesy, Oliver Motors)

Carburetor high-speed metering valve must be opened in order for fuel to reach carburetor. Fixed carburetor jets found on many modern motors do not require any adjustment. (Courtesy, Mercury Motors)

Be careful when checking the ball-check valve, for you may have built up pressure in your lines and may get a face full of fuel for your efforts. Keep in mind, too, that when investigating fuel troubles, you should make sure that neither you nor your passengers are smoking nor that there is any other means that might start a fire should fuel or fuel vapors be released into the boat.

In checking the valve at the connector end, use a blunt instrument, press against the spring pressure while a crew member squeezes the priming bulb, directing any flow from the fitting overboard. With a pressurized system, direct the fitting overboard and follow the same procedure, though pressure from the fuel tank will force fuel through the fitting as soon as the valve is unseated.

8–9. With a pressurized fuel system, two synthetic rubber tubes are used. One tube carries air pressure from the powerhead to the tank; the other line pumps fuel from the tank to the motor. These two lines are fused together, and the connector joins the fuel-air lines to corresponding fittings on the powerhead. The air line leads to a crankcase check valve, the fuel line to the carburetor. These connectors are usually marked "air" and "fuel" so that they cannot be crossed. However, it is possible if lines have been damaged for the connectors to be switched. This would be immediately apparent after any repairs to lines had been made, because the system will not function unless air and fuel flow are both unrestricted. To check for switched connectors, pump up three to five pounds pressure with the pump button on the tank and depress the air valve on the line. If fuel comes out, the lines have been reversed and you should take the lines and connector back to your dealer and raise hell.

The most likely cause for no pressure in the air tank is due to a loose filler cap, cracked filler cap, or faulty filler cap gasket. These three should be checked in that order.

A loose connection or leak in the air hose, either at the fittings or along the length of the line, can be another cause of trouble. Leaking lines can be repaired in one of two ways: if the leak is close to either the tank or to the removable fuel line connector, the leaky sections can be cut off, foreshortening the line. Leaks in the midsections of the line, which if cut off would cause overly short leads, can be repaired. Cut two sections of short, approximately 2″, pieces of copper tubing.

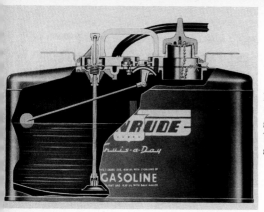

Pressurized-type fuel tank (cutaway view). Prior to starting, pressure must be built up by rapidly depressing push button to left of carrying handle.

These splicing sections should have an outer dimension the same as the inner dimension of the flexible tubing. They should be placed in the tubes, so that the cut ends of the tubes meet at the center of the copper splicing sections. The cut ends should then be pushed together over the copper splices and secured with hose clamps. Even if only one of the twin lines is leaking, both must be shortened equally since the lines are fused together lengthwise.

Some nonpressurized remote fuel tanks are fitted with quick connector joints at both ends of the line. When replacing these, be certain that the primer bulb is located so that the shorter length of fuel line is adjacent to the motor.

10. Fuel pump failure in a pressurized system is most likely to be caused by a damaged pump diaphragm in the fuel tank or by a clogged fuel tank screen inlet. When pushing on the pump button to build up desired pressure, do not continue pumping when resistance is felt. As pressure is built up, fuel is forced through the system, fills the float bowl in the carburetor until the bowl fills, and the rising float closes the supply valve that permits fuel to enter the bowl. It is this continued pumping after pressure has been obtained that may cause the diaphragm in the fuel tank pumping system to be ruptured.

Nonpressurized systems make use of displacement-type pumps operated by alternate vacuum and compression impulses in the motor's crankcase. The fuel supplies of some nonpressurized vacuum systems do not have a priming bulb but have a plunger-type primer on the fuel tank. Priming in this case is

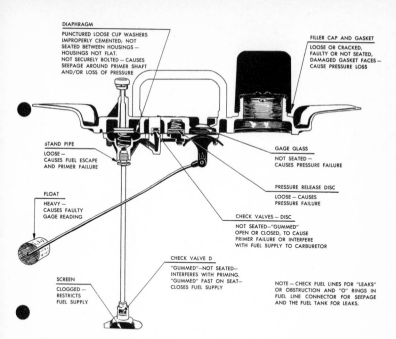

DIAPHRAGM
PUNCTURED LOOSE CUP WASHERS
IMPROPERLY CEMENTED; NOT
SEATED BETWEEN HOUSINGS —
HOUSINGS NOT FLAT.
NOT SECURELY BOLTED — CAUSES
SEEPAGE AROUND PRIMER SHAFT
AND/OR LOSS OF PRESSURE

FILLER CAP AND GASKET
LOOSE OR CRACKED,
FAULTY OR NOT SEATED,
DAMAGED GASKET FACES —
CAUSE PRESSURE LOSS

STAND PIPE
LOOSE —
CAUSES FUEL ESCAPE
AND PRIMER FAILURE

GAGE GLASS
NOT SEATED —
CAUSES PRESSURE FAILURE

PRESSURE RELEASE DISC
LOOSE — CAUSES
PRESSURE FAILURE

FLOAT
HEAVY —
CAUSES FAULTY
GAGE READING

CHECK VALVES — DISC
NOT SEATED—"GUMMED"
OPEN OR CLOSED, TO CAUSE
PRIMER FAILURE OR INTERFERE
WITH FUEL SUPPLY TO CARBURETOR

CHECK VALVE D
"GUMMED"—NOT SEATED—
INTERFERES WITH PRIMING.
"GUMMED" FAST ON SEAT—
CLOSES FUEL SUPPLY

SCREEN
CLOGGED —
RESTRICTS
FUEL SUPPLY

NOTE — CHECK FUEL LINES FOR "LEAKS"
OR OBSTRUCTION AND "O" RINGS IN
FUEL LINE CONNECTOR FOR SEEPAGE
AND THE FUEL TANK FOR LEAKS.

Troubleshooting chart for a typical pressurized fuel tank.

done by pushing up and down on the plunger until resistance is felt.

11–12. Inspect fuel filters. These are usually glass bowls fitted with a wing nut so that the bowl can be easily removed. Water accumulations can be detected by a variance in color of the liquid in the bowl. Some bowls also contain a filter element made of porous stone or a synthetic material. Both the bowl and the filter are simple to clean by flushing in a container of fresh gasoline.

13. Some carburetors are fitted with a screen or strainer. This must be located somewhere on the carburetor body between the source of fuel supply and the carburetor bowl. Unless you are sure that your carburetor is fitted with one, better not tamper with the carburetor except in an emergency. Leave this to the experienced repairman.

14. Check the high-speed metering valve and open it to your normal operating position.

If fuel is reaching the carburetor, your motor has spark, and the motor fails to start:

POSSIBLE CAUSES:

1. Flooding.
2. Choke failure.
3. Water in the gasoline.
4. Dirt or restriction in the carburetor jets.

REMEDIES:

1–2. If the carburetor is flooding, it may be due to a number of different faults—the most probable ones being a stuck choke linkage, a stuck carburetor bowl float, accidentally closed choke, a fuel-logged float, improper seating of the high-speed metering jet needle, an excess of fuel tank pressure in a pressurized system, or an improperly functioning fuel pump causing excessive pressure.

Excessive fuel tank pressure or an improperly functioning fuel pump are jobs for the skilled outboard mechanic. In an emergency, release pressure at the remote tank, pump only to two to three pounds, and try again to start. If pressure does not build up excessively again, the trouble probably was caused by a temporarily stuck pressure relief valve.

The first and most obvious remedy for flooding is to check the choke mechanism. If the choke is of a manual design and the motor was still warm when it stopped and refused to restart, continue to rope the motor over without choking. In

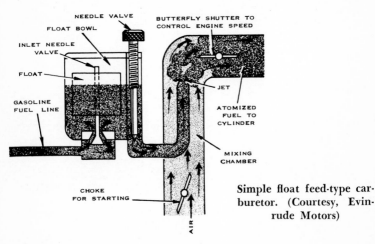

Simple float feed-type carburetor. (Courtesy, Evinrude Motors)

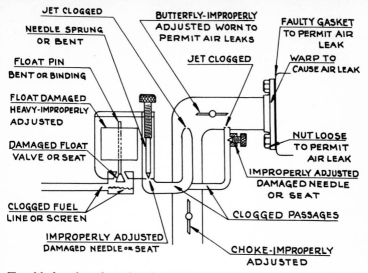

JET CLOGGED

NEEDLE SPRUNG OR BENT

FLOAT PIN BENT OR BINDING

FLOAT DAMAGED HEAVY-IMPROPERLY ADJUSTED

DAMAGED FLOAT VALVE OR SEAT

CLOGGED FUEL LINE OR SCREEN

IMPROPERLY ADJUSTED DAMAGED NEEDLE OR SEAT

BUTTERFLY-IMPROPERLY ADJUSTED WORN TO PERMIT AIR LEAKS

JET CLOGGED

FAULTY GASKET TO PERMIT AIR LEAK

WARP TO CAUSE AIR LEAK

NUT LOOSE TO PERMIT AIR LEAK

IMPROPERLY ADJUSTED DAMAGED NEEDLE OR SEAT

CLOGGED PASSAGES

CHOKE-IMPROPERLY ADJUSTED

Troubleshooting chart for simplified version of a carburetor found on many small two-cycle engines. (Courtesy, Johnson Motors)

cases of excessive flooding, close the high-speed needle valve, rope the engine over briskly to clear out excess fuel, then open the needle valve to proper setting and try again. In cases of extreme flooding, you may have to remove spark plugs, rope the engine over to free the cylinders of excess fuel, replace the plugs, and repeat the starting procedure, this time without choking.

Electrically starting outboards have varying types of choke mechanisms. On key-starting motors, a partial turn of the key will activate the starter motor. Twisting the key farther will automatically activate the choke at the same time the starter motor rotates the flywheel. Push-button-type starters sometimes incorporate two positions of the button. A slight depressing of the starter button will cause automatic choking. Consult your operations manual and be certain you are following the recommended procedure and are not inadvertently choking the motor.

Occasionally, carburetor bowl floats will stick due to an accumulation of varnish or lacquer on the inside of the bowl. If fuel continues to flow from the carburetor air intake when you are not choking the motor, an improperly functioning bowl float may well be the cause. Tap lightly on the side of the carburetor bowl with a blunt instrument, such as the handle of a screwdriver. This usually will free a stuck float and allow it to rise to its proper level.

Carburetor floats are constructed either of cork or are of airtight cylindrical or doughnut-shaped brass construction. Corrosive elements in the fuel may eat tiny pinholes in floats, causing them to leak and become fuel logged. Faulty floats must be replaced.

3. Pull spark plugs and check for droplets of water on the electrodes. If there is, and the water is reaching the plugs through the fuel induction system, purge the fuel lines, drain carburetor bowl, and try again. If water continues to short out the plugs, you will have to throw away the contaminated fuel and start with fresh fuel.

4. Dirt in carburetor jets or an improperly seated high-speed metering jet can cause an excess of fuel flow. Removing the needle valve and blowing through the jet will rid jets of dirt.

Damage to metering jet needle is more serious. This occurs if the needles are turned fully inward too tightly, causing the tapered tip of the needle to be cut by the seat. It is recommended that the high-speed needle be inspected about once a year and if a groove has been cut into the tapered point, the needle should be replaced.

If the motor starts but the engine idles erratically:

POSSIBLE CAUSES:

1. A faulty carburetor gasket or carburetor body securing bolts loose at the carburetor flange.
2. Dirt or water in the fuel.
3. Reed or leaf valves broken or improperly seated.
4. An incorrect carburetor float level.
5. Damaged throttle shutter.
6. Improperly adjusted idling metering valve.

REMEDIES:

1. Check the carburetor securing bolts and be certain that they are drawn up snugly. Look for evidence of fuel leakage around the carburetor flange, and, if any is apparent, then the gasket should be replaced.
2. Since gasoline and water will not mix, water in the fuel can be detected by catching a little of the fuel in the palm of

your hand and inspecting the liquid for any separation. Since gasoline will evaporate rapidly, blow on the fuel, and, if separate droplets remain in the palm of your hand after a few moments, this would be evidence of water. The solution is to drain the fuel system and start over again with fresh fuel.

3. Broken or improperly seated leaf valves usually may be detected by fuel spraying from the carburetor throat. Replacement of reeds is a job for the expert.

4. An incorrect carburetor float level, either too high or too low, probably is caused by a lacquer build-up on the valve and valve seat, causing the float to stick. An accumulation of lacquer on the float body also will cause sticking, or the float will not reach normal level and the engine will fail to attain full power because of fuel flow starvation.

Any float malfunction calls for disassembly and careful cleaning or replacement of damaged parts. Lacquer thinner or alcohol will remove this build-up, though care should be taken that lacquer thinner does not come in contact with neoprene fuel lines, fittings, or any synthetic materials used as a packing agent in carburetor valves. Better leave float jobs to your repairman.

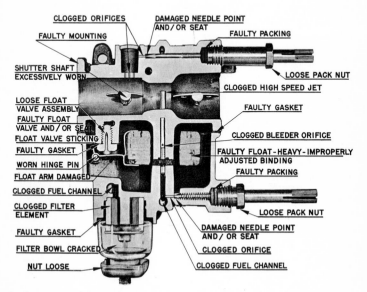

Carburetor with various potential trouble spots indicated (cut-away view). (Courtesy, Johnson Motors)

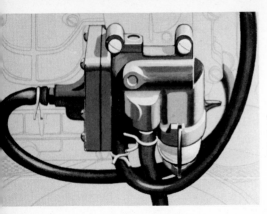

Typical crankcase-operated fuel pump used on a non-pressurized-type fuel system.

5. Damaged or improperly functioning throttle shutter calls for replacement.

6. The idle metering valve usually can be spotted as that slotted screw adjustment fitted with a coil spring. The motor should be properly warmed and the high-speed metering adjustment correctly made before attempting to adjust the idling valve. Then with the motor in neutral gear in the slow position, first turn the needle inward until the motor starts to slow down as the mixture becomes too rich. Most metering valves actually control the amount of air mixed with a fixed jet secondary fuel supply. As the motor fires unevenly due to an overly rich mixture (i.e. an amount of air less than required), turn the screw outward, that is counterclockwise, until the motor fires evenly.

Some carburetors are fitted with a slow-speed metering jet which controls a combined mixture of air and fuel. The adjustment on this type operates just the reverse. The larger the needle opening, that is the farther the needle is turned in a counterclockwise direction, the richer the mixture. This variance in design is not of major importance since your ultimate purpose will be to attain smooth running, and you can do this by trying adjustments in either direction. For a final setting, keep the adjustment a bit on the rich side rather than on the lean side to prevent stalling.

The altitude at which you operate your outboard motor has a decided effect on its developed power. Any internal-combustion engine develops more power at sea level. This is so because the air at sea level is denser and contains a greater amount of oxygen in any given quantity than does the less dense air at higher altitudes. The trailboater is most likely to encounter problems caused by varying air density, and he should expect diminishing performance as operating altitudes increase. He should compensate for this operational phenomenon by leaning carburetor adjustments as altitudes increase.

If your motor is of a type that is equipped with fixed carburetor jets allowing for no high-speed metering adjustments, replacement jets are available for varying altitudes—each set of jets usually covering a range of approximately 2,500' to 3,000', and these are carried by marine dealers.

It is recommended that every outboarder prepare a fuel consumption chart for varying load and weather conditions. This will prove to be an invaluable asset in planning fuel requirements for cruises of varying lengths, and it also will make it possible for the outboarder to spot rapidly any sudden and marked increase in fuel consumption, which may be an indication of carburetor problems.

The outboarder noting a sudden gas consumption increase should first check for leaks in his gas tank, fuel lines, and connections, for these obviously will present a fire hazard. High gas consumption also can be caused by ignition weaknesses, poor cylinder compression, faulty crankcase compression, an excessive build-up of carbon in the exhaust system, or an improperly adjusted or worn throttle linkage.

5. Ignition System Troubleshooting

The ignition system of the outboard motor consists of an electrical generating unit called a magneto. The most commonplace magneto is mounted under the flywheel of the powerhead. It consists of an armature plate on which are secured such basic components as coil, condenser, breaker points plus permanent magnets built into the flywheel, or a magnet rotor mounted on the crankshaft. The magneto is self-contained and does not require any accessory electrical source such as a storage battery or a dry cell to produce its electrical energy. The energy is created by the rotation of the crankshaft and flywheel. The operation is extremely simple.

The pole pieces secured to the inner surface of the flywheel or the crankshaft-keyed rotor rotate rapidly past a set of metal heel plates which cause a magnetic field to be built up about the coil. The coil is made up of a primary and secondary winding. The induced magnetic field causes a current to flow through the primary winding. When the flow of this induced current is suddenly interrupted, lines of magnetic force are produced, causing exceptionally high voltage to be induced into the secondary windings of the coil. The secondary windings of the coil are connected by high-tension leads to spark plugs. When the sudden charge of high voltage is produced, it flows through the high-tension lead to the plug, jumps the plug gap, which in turn ignites the compressed charge in the cylinders.

The condenser which is linked with the secondary winding of the coil serves as a temporary storage for the secondary current released by the primary winding. This stored current in turn is released when the charge is induced into the secondary winding, adding to the intensity of the electrical charge flowing to the spark plugs.

The breaker points are secured to a bracket on the stator plate. Their opening and closing (breaking) action is caused by a cam located on the crankshaft, machined into the flywheel or in some other way made a permanent part of the rotation of the engine's crankshaft.

This sounds uncomplicated and the two-cycle ignition system is comparatively simple. Component parts, however, must be in good functioning order to produce a good fat spark—and the spark must be produced at the proper time in relationship to the piston travel and compression of the vaporized gases in the cylinder for the engine to function at full power.

Faulty ignition can create motor problems ranging from a failure to start to powerhead knocking, rough operation, high-speed misfiring and engine backfiring.

If your outboard motor fails to start and the seat of the trouble does not appear to be with your fuel supply:

Possible Causes:

1. Faulty spark plugs.
2. Faulty high-tension leads.
3. Breaker point malfunctioning.
4. Armature plate wiring failure.
5. Condenser failure.
6. Coil or other magneto component failure.

Remedies:

1. First remove the spark plug and inspect its condition. The most commonplace spark plug failure is due to fouling of the electrodes. This fortunately is mostly temporary in nature and can be easily remedied. Gas or fuel fouling of a plug usually can be identified by dark, fluffy, black deposits covering the entire firing end of the spark plug. This excessive carbon ac-

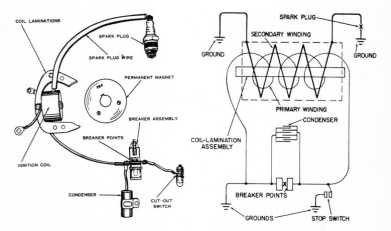

(*Left*) Typical permanent magnet type two-cycle ignition system. (Courtesy, Evinrude Motors)

(*Right*) Typical outboard magneto ignition system. (Courtesy, Evinrude Motors)

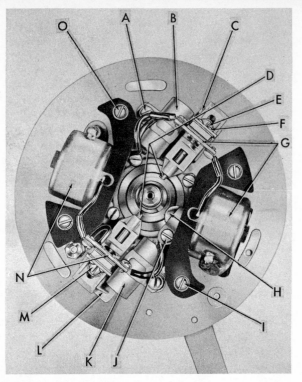

Magneto assembly of a permanent magnet type: **(A)** Condenser screw; **(B)** condenser; **(C)** adjusting notches; **(D)** breaker push rods; **(E)** breaker adjusting screw; **(F)** contact points; **(G)** port breaker points and front coil fire lower cylinder; **(H)** felt oiler; **(I)** coil mounting screw; **(J)** four "hold down" or tension screws; **(K)** condenser; **(L)** adjusting notches; **(M)** breaker adjusting screw; **(N)** starboard breaker points and rear coil fire upper cylinder; **(O)** coil mounting screw. (Courtesy, Evinrude Motors)

cumulation also may have a wet gummy appearance. The deposits are the result of incomplete combustion which can be caused by an overly rich fuel-air mixture, a spark plug of the wrong heat range, wrong spark plug gap, or faulty ignition.

A spark plug which is functioning properly and is of the proper heat range will produce a rusty brown to light tan coloration on the ceramic insulator (at the firing end). Burned spark plugs will have a white or burned blistered appearance of the insulator tip and may have badly eroded electrodes. The burned plugs are a result of overheating, improper spark timing, poor fuel, or an overly hot plug heat range.

Spark plugs are made in a variety of heat ranges to satisfy different operating conditions, varying engine designs, fuels, and other variables. Heat range refers to the capacity of a spark plug to conduct heat away from its firing end. Spark plugs with long lean firing ends to their insulators transfer heat slowly. They are know as "hot range" plugs and are used where continued idling will be experienced, such as in trolling, for light load conditions, stop-and-go activity. Spark plugs with short stubby insulators transfer heat more rapidly. They are used for heavy-duty activity, high-speed activity, racing, and conditions which will cause greater engine heat. These are referred to as "cold range" plugs.

Every spark plug manufacturer marks his spark plugs with a coded number, letter, or combinations of the two. This marking indicates the heat range of the plug. Your operational manual will recommend the proper heat range plug for you to use in your motor.

Your manual will also specify the proper spark plug gap, that is the opening between the center and side electrodes at the firing end of the plug. Both proper heat range and proper plug gap are vital to efficient motor performance.

Two-cycle engines, since they combine lubricant with gasoline, call for a special type of spark plug to reduce fouling possibilities. If in doubt about the proper selection of plug to use in your motor, consult your outboard dealer.

The spark plugs must be maintained in good operating condition, insulators clean, free of oil, water, uncracked. The plugs should be seated properly in the plug hole and fitted with a gasket in good condition. As a usual practice when fitting the motor with new plugs and gaskets, screw the plug into the hole in a clockwise direction finger tight, then draw up with a wrench a half to three-quarters of a turn. Don't use undue pressure on the wrench or you may ruin the gasket or strip or damage the spark plug hole threads.

It is a good idea to carry spare, replacement spark plugs, because they cannot be thoroughly cleaned underway without special equipment. To clean fouled plugs, soak them overnight in a can of acetone, then scrub the electrodes and the insulator with a brush. Lighter fluid makes an ideal solvent, and with a cloth moistened with lighter fluid you will be able to clean a moderately fouled spark plug underway. Badly fouled plugs,

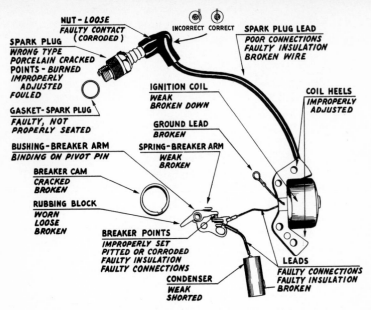

NUT - LOOSE
FAULTY CONTACT
(CORRODED)

INCORRECT   CORRECT

SPARK PLUG LEAD
POOR CONNECTIONS
FAULTY INSULATION
BROKEN WIRE

SPARK PLUG
WRONG TYPE
PORCELAIN CRACKED
POINTS - BURNED
IMPROPERLY
ADJUSTED
FOULED

GASKET - SPARK PLUG
FAULTY, NOT
PROPERLY SEATED

IGNITION COIL
WEAK
BROKEN DOWN

COIL HEELS
IMPROPERLY
ADJUSTED

GROUND LEAD
BROKEN

BUSHING - BREAKER ARM
BINDING ON PIVOT PIN

SPRING - BREAKER ARM
WEAK
BROKEN

BREAKER CAM
CRACKED
BROKEN

RUBBING BLOCK
WORN
LOOSE
BROKEN

BREAKER POINTS
IMPROPERLY SET
PITTED OR CORRODED
FAULTY INSULATION
FAULTY CONNECTIONS

LEADS
FAULTY CONNECTIONS
FAULTY INSULATION
BROKEN

CONDENSER
WEAK
SHORTED

Magneto check chart. (Courtesy, Johnson Motors)

Automotive-type ignition used on many of the larger horsepower motors is gear, belt, or chain driven. Those used on Mercury motors are easily removed by taking out three bolts.

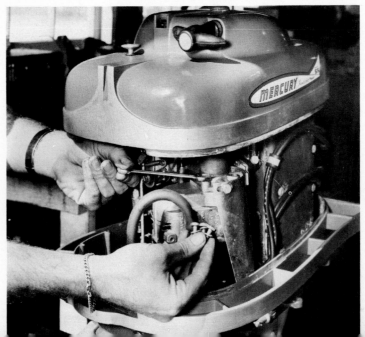

with carbon accumulation gathered around the insulator well back in the body of the plug, will require special cleaning, but can be returned to usable condition. Any automotive service station has equipment for cleaning plugs, alternately sand and air blasting them on a special plug cleaning machine.

Gapping the electrodes of spark plugs is a very simple procedure. It calls for a round wire gapping gauge which you can buy for 25¢ or less from your marine dealer or an auto parts supply house. Keep in mind that when adjusting the gap, adjust only the side or ground electrode. Always check the gap even of new plugs, since varying models of motors call for different gapping, usually anywhere from .018″ to .030″. New plugs usually are set only approximately at between .030″ and .035″.

2. The first check that should be made when you suspect ignition failure is to determine whether or not the magneto is introducing an electrical charge to the spark plug through the high-tension leads. Remove each spark plug lead from the plug in turn. Hold the high-tension lead wire so that the contact clip is about $\frac{3}{16}$″ to $\frac{1}{4}$″ away from the plug. Do not hold the metal clip in your fingers but grip the high-tension lead by the insulation. Then have someone pull briskly on the engine's starter cord. A fat, blue spark should jump the gap if current is reaching the end of the high-tension lead.

Make sure that the high-tension leads are firmly connected with the spark plugs. The contact clips or "sparkies" (spiral wire coils imbedded in L-shaped rubber insulators designed to protect the contact from exposure to spray or dampness) may not have been pressed onto the end of the spark plug firmly enough to assure a positive electrical contact.

3. Next to faulty spark plugs the most frequent cause of ignition failure is breaker points improperly adjusted or fouled. Naturally, to get at the breaker points, just as any components of the stator plate, the flywheel must be removed.

The first check of the points should be the gap, i.e., distance between points when they are fully opened. Slowly rotate the flywheel until the cam is positioned so that the high spot on the cam causes the breaker points to be fully opened. That occurs when the insulated rubbing block of the breaker point assembly is in contact with the highest point of the cam. Proper breaker point clearances will vary depending on the ignition system, model and make of the motor. The manufacturer's instructions should be followed implicitly in making the proper adjustments to the points.

Entire magneto assembly can be removed in a few minutes and taken to dealer for repair or adjustment.

However, whenever points require adjusting, it is well to clean them first. Inspect the points under the glow of a flashlight, and if the two points are not wholly squared or if, when the points are held open, the point surfaces are pitted, oil filmed, or covered with a powdery deposit, they require cleaning. Fold a narrow strip of 00 sandpaper so that the abrasive is exposed on both sides. Place this between the points, squeeze them together, then draw the sandpaper upward through the tensed points. Repeat this procedure several times. Then with a clean strip of nonlinty paper, clean the residue of sand from the face of the points.

Do not use any abrasive paper containing metallic grains, such as emery cloth, for the tiny metal particles, being conductors, may create a short circuit.

Test the spring tension of the points. If it seems weak, consult your dealer. He can check this with a spring-tension scale so the tension can be properly balanced or the springs replaced if the temper of the spring is gone.

Finally set the points to the manufacturer's gap specification.

4. Inspect the wiring of the armature plate for loose or broken connections. Any loose connection should be tightened; broken connections will call for soldering. When soldering ignition wiring do not use an acid flux, because acids can produce corrosion or eat through the insulation of the coils or condensers.

Unless you have had experience, better leave the soldering of connections of the ignition system to an expert since the excessive heat of a soldering iron also can cause damage to the windings in the coil or the insulation of the laminates of the condenser.

5–6. A check for a condenser or coil failure must be made by the outboard repairman who will have specialized ignition testing equipment.

If your outboard motor misfires in an idling range:

Possible Causes:

1. Incorrect spark plug gap.
2. Spark plugs of the wrong heat range.
3. Loose spark plugs or damaged spark plug gaskets.
4. Leaking or shorting high-tension leads.
5. Incorrect breaker point gap.
6. Sticking breaker arm.
7. Breaker points not synchronized.
8. Spark timing overly advanced.
9. Loose or worn cam.
10. Weak coil or condenser.
11. Weak armature magnets.

Keep in mind, however, that when the engine runs roughly or misfires at idle, you should first check the fuel system and suspect dirt or water in the fuel, improper float level in the carburetor, or improperly adjusted idling jet.

Remedies:

1. Set plug gap to that electrode clearance recommended by the manufacturer.

2. Use plugs of the heat range recommended by the manufacturer. However, as an engine wears and piston rings gradually lose their ability to retain the full-designed compression of the engine, it may be necessary to switch to the next hottest range spark plug.

3. Damaged spark plug gaskets or excessive carbon or foreign matter on the gasket seats may cause a compression loss through incomplete sealing as can improperly tightened spark plugs. Either of these faults may result in hard starting as well as erratic performance.

4. Oil-soaked high-tension leads or high-tension leads covered with cracked, dried, and rotted insulating material may

Occasionally ignition trouble is caused by spring-type high-tension lead connector not making full contact. (Courtesy, Evinrude Motors)

leak much of the high-tension charge to nearby metallic parts of the motor. Such tired leads obviously should be replaced by new ones. However, occasionally internal breaks can occur in the high-tension lead while the insulation still appears to be faultless. Your outboard dealer will have a probe-type instrument with which he can test the entire length of your high-tension lead wiring, detect any leaks, or be assured that the leads are leak free.

5. See discussion under outboard motor fails to start in this chapter.

6. The movable breaker arm commonly is designed to rotate on a pivot post. A bit of grit or foreign matter may cause this to stick. Periodically you should lubricate breaker arm pivot posts with a light coating of petroleum jelly.

7. The breaker points must start to open at the proper sequence in each piston's upward movement on compression stroke in addition to opening to the prescribed gap measurement. For example, on alternate firing twin motors, the points must start to open or break exactly 180 degrees apart. On a three-cylinder motor, the points must be synchronized so that they break 120 degrees apart. Alternate firing fours must break 90 degrees apart, and alternate firing sixes, exactly 60 degrees apart. Any variation from this will cause erratic performance and power loss. You or your mechanic can make this adjustment with the aid of a degree wheel or scribe marks.

8. In addition to it being necessary that the points "make and break" at a precise number of degrees apart, depending on the number of cylinders in the motor, the spark must also occur at the proper time in relation to the travel of the piston on the compression stroke. During the ignition process a spark occurs, ignites the compressed fuel, and, as the fuel burns, the heat of the flame causes the gases to expand rapidly. These expanding gases exert pressure on the crown of the piston, forcing it away from the burned gases and the top of the cylinder. At slow speed, the pistons slide in and out of the cylinder more slowly. Because of this, the burned gases have more time to exert their influence during the cycle of the stroke. During slow speed running, the spark must be retarded; that is the spark must be created at a time when the piston is closer to the top of its movement toward the head of the cylinder. If ignition is not retarded, the burning gases will exert their pressure on the piston before it reaches the end of its stroke, and the engine, in extreme cases of overadvanced ignition, will come to a stop because the power impulse would be exerted in such a way as to reverse the piston's movement before it has completed its full stroke.

The timing of ignition to piston movement is expressed in one of two ways: either as the number of degrees of rotation b.t.d.c. (before top dead center) of the piston stroke that igni-

A worn or loose fitting rotor can alter ignition timing or create erratic ignition. Replace worn rotors. (Courtesy, Bendix Corporation)

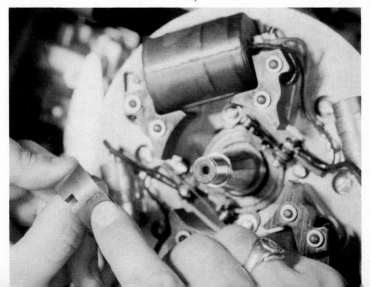

Weak or faulty coils or condensers should be checked by an outboard specialist. Faulty components must be replaced. (Courtesy, Bendix Corporation)

tion occurs, or in fractions of an inch before the piston arrives at top dead center or at its full compression point.

You can see by this that the entire sequence of ignition must be carefully timed, that not only must the spark occur at evenly spaced intervals so that each piston movement is given its ignition at the same point but that the ignition must also occur at the right time. For example, an alternate firing twin engine might have points properly adjusted to the right breaker gap, the points timed so that they open and close exactly 180 degrees apart, and yet the sparks may come too soon, causing rough idling, overheating, engine knocking and preignition, or too late, causing a power loss.

Overly slow timing of ignition is not unlike the batter who is able to connect with the ball but swings too late and keeps fouling the ball off into the stands along first base. The overly advanced ignition could be likened to the baseball player who constantly pulls his hits into the stands along third base. Properly timed ignition gives full power at all throttle openings and is good for everything from a bunt to a home run, all laid down right through the center slot.

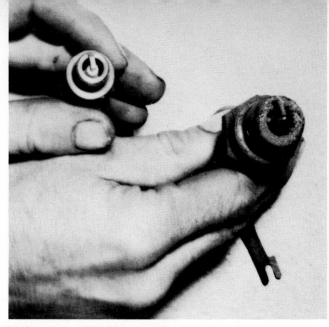

Major cause of ignition troubles is fouled plugs. Carry a spare set!

A motor which has gotten out of time through wearing of parts or other causes should be retimed by an expert. To do it properly requires specialized equipment and infinite patience.

9. A loose or worn cam creates erratic ignition. The loose cam permits a variation in the make and break contacts; the worn cam changes timing. Replace worn cams or shim them to prevent end play.

10–11. Weak coils or condensers require specialized testing equipment for detection. Weak armature magnets are a rarity. They are usually caused by an accidental blow to the flywheel or dropping the flywheel. Magnets can be recharged by a specialist.

If the engine misses fire at high speed:

POSSIBLE CAUSES:

1. Weak breaker arm spring.
2. Coil shorts through insulation.
3. Faulty breaker points.
4. Wrong heat range spark plugs.
5. Spark plug gap too wide.
6. Overly advanced ignition timing.

REMEDIES:

Check ignition factors only after first being certain that the high-speed jet of the carburetor has not been adjusted overly lean. Excessive carbon in cylinders or poor compression can also cause high-speed misfiring. The ignition system shortcomings leading to high-speed operational problems have already been discussed.

All spark plugs will wear out ultimately and should be replaced. The life span of a spark plug depends not only on its care but other factors. The exposed portion of the insulator should be kept free of moisture, grease, and dirt. Under no conditions should paint be applied to the plug's insulator, for any foreign deposits will cause shorting across the exterior surface of the insulator between the terminal post at the end of the insulator and the body of the spark plug grounding the spark to the cylinder.

Since the condition of the spark plug is the final determining factor as to the efficiency of the ignition system, it is recommended that you don't cut corners by buying cheap off-brand plugs. Be wary of claims by manufacturers of "freak" plugs; few of the unconventional type have proved to be satisfactory for outboard operation.

Breaker points should be cleaned periodically and adjusted carefully to manufacturer's specifications for a particular motor. (Courtesy, Mercury Motors)

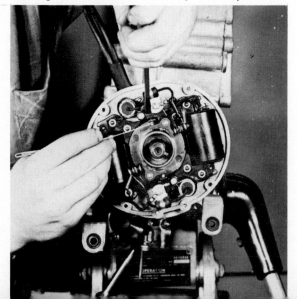

Much spark plug trouble is caused by lead fouling of the electrodes and insulator tip. This is caused by the use of excessive tetraethyl antiknock compound in high octane rated automotive fuels designed for high-compression automotive use. The outboard motor does not require special high octane rated gasoline. It is recommended that "marine white" gasoline, which has no lead addition, be used. Do not confuse this type with the white gasoline sold for farm implement use and cooking. The use of "marine white" will eliminate plug fouling caused by lead content in the fuel.

It is recommended, too, that you do not substitute non-two-cycle oils but rather stick to those specially compounded for outboard use. The use of good quality two-cycle engine oil will offer longer spark plug life and in general will help keep your power plant's innards free of varnish, gum, and carbon deposits.

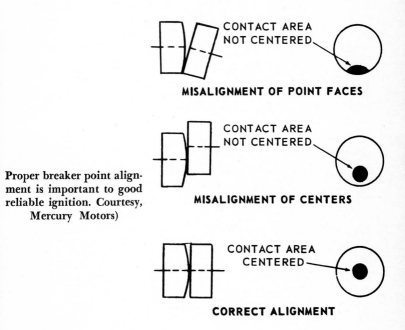

CONTACT AREA NOT CENTERED

MISALIGNMENT OF POINT FACES

CONTACT AREA NOT CENTERED

Proper breaker point alignment is important to good reliable ignition. Courtesy, Mercury Motors)

MISALIGNMENT OF CENTERS

CONTACT AREA CENTERED

CORRECT ALIGNMENT

6. Powerhead Maintenance
and Troubleshooting

The basic powerhead components of an outboard motor are crankcase, crankshaft, flywheel bearings to support the crankshaft and provide lessened friction during rotation, a valve assembly—usually reed valves or leaf valves—cylinders, pistons, and connecting rods.

Bearings in the powerhead are vitally important. They offer support to the revolving and reciprocating parts and reduce friction. They are divided into two categories: friction and nonfriction bearings.

The friction-type bearings are bushings or cylindrical sleeves constructed of bronze. These offer support but are not overly efficient in preventing friction. The nonfriction type bearings are more complex. They usually are constructed with a steel inner and outer race within which a row of rollers, needles, or steel balls roll. Steel needle bearings often are used on the crank pin end of connecting rods and also are used on the wrist pin end of rods.

The friction-type bearings or bushings seldom are found in other than motors of modest horsepower since the stress of higher loads on larger horsepower motors calls for the nonfriction type.

Cleanliness is one of the key secrets to long life of any outboard motor. By cleanliness I mean a careful screening of all fuel to prevent the introduction of any foreign matter into the internal parts of the powerhead. Grit or tiny grains of sand can quickly score any of the internal surfaces, resulting in loss of compression, rapid wear of rotating and reciprocating parts, and ultimate failure due to excessive heat and sloppy operation due to excessive wear.

Dirt, dust, and grit can be introduced into the powerhead of the outboard motor as a result of improper protection during over-the-road transportation. The powerhead of motors transported in car trunks or in the luggage compartment of station wagons should be protected from swirling drafts which can blow foreign matter through the carburetor intake manifolds. One simple protective measure is to wrap the motor in an old sheet so that the entire powerhead assembly is shrouded.

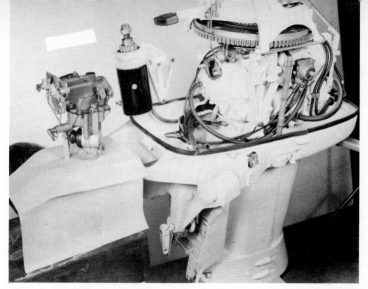

A cowl-removed shot showing electric starter and carburetor assembly unbolted. Powerhead proper incorporates crankcase assembly and cylinder block assembly. (Courtesy, Johnson Motors)

Profile view, with cowl removed, of a six-cylinder-in-line engine. (Courtesy, Mercury Motors)

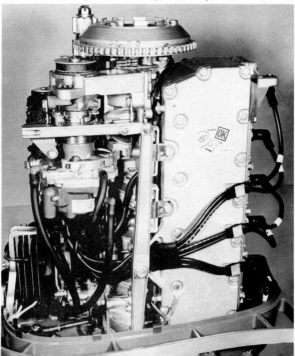

In transporting over the road with the motor mounted on the boat, the same precautions should apply. Most dealers carry tailor-made outboard motor covers constructed of fabric or plastic and designed with just this purpose in mind. Remember that even though your motor is cowled, provisions have been made for the motor to get a sufficient volume of air for proper carburetion. If you'll check over the motor's cowling, you'll find that it is not completely sealed, that there are slots or holes somewhere in the cowling to allow entry of air. These same holes will permit dust and dirt to get under the cowling.

Troubleshooting your engine's powerhead, like troubleshooting the ignition and fuel system, may be broken down into a number of different categories. Many powerhead malfunctions can be repaired only by the outboard repair specialist or the owner with special skill. Yet an ability to analyze possible trouble and to have the fault corrected before greater damage occurs will save you from major breakdowns underway or the frustration of motor failure at an inopportune time. Failures or malfunctioning which can be attributed to fuel or ignition have already been covered.

Let's look next to powerhead noises.

If your outboard motor operates but you hear knocking sounds:

POSSIBLE CAUSES:

1. Loose flywheel.
2. Excessive crankshaft end play.
3. Excessive bearing clearance.
4. Excessive bearing wear.
5. Bent or twisted crankshaft.
6. Worn crankshaft journals.
7. Broken crankshaft.
8. Bent or twisted connecting rods.
9. Loose or bent wrist pin.
10. Excessive connecting rod bearing clearance.
11. Misaligned connecting rod caps.
12. Damaged or out-of-round cylinder.
13. Worn or damaged pistons.
14. Excessive ring groove clearance or broken piston ring.
15. Excessive carbon in head of cylinder, on crown of piston, or both.

REMEDIES:

1. Check the flywheel retaining nut. If loose, it should be drawn up tightly, preferably with a torque wrench, to manufacturer's torque recommendations. Remember that many outboard motor components are constructed of aluminum alloys. Though the flywheel and crankshaft, of course, are steel, use restraint in drawing any fastenings overly tight to prevent stripping threads or breaking parts.

Many models of outboard motors require a variety of special tools for internal repairs such as flywheel pullers, bearing and water pump pullers, piston ring retainers, and others. Unless you make a hobby of doing your own repairs and have these special tools, it will be cheaper and easier for you to have major repair work done by the factory-trained outboard motor repairman.

2. Excessive crankshaft end play may be detected by lifting on the outer edges of the flywheel. There should be some motion here. The range will vary depending on the model of motor, from about .008″ to .016″. Excessive end play usually will have been caused by wear and will require shims or spacers.

3–6. These can best be checked for by removing spark plugs to relieve compression. Ground the spark plug high-tension leads to prevent overloading ignition components. Shift the engine into neutral position if it is a gearshift model. Rotate the flywheel, and by ear and feel, note whether there seem to

Crankshaft, connecting rod, and piston assembly of a Johnson V-4.

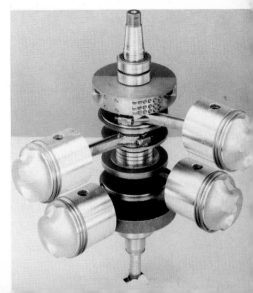

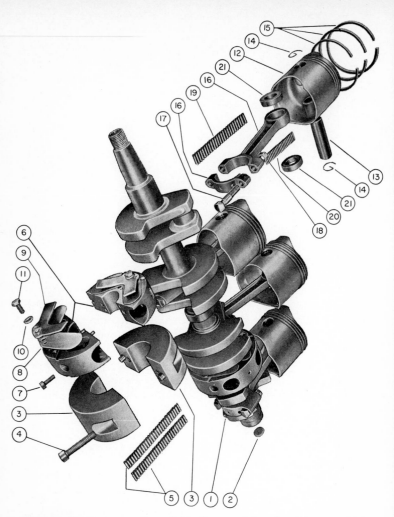

Crankshaft, piston, and reed block assembly of a Mercury four-cylinder-in-line motor: (1) Crankshaft; (2) felt oiler, drive-shaft spline; (3) center main bearing assembly; (4) screw, center main bearing assembly; (5) needle roller, center main bearing; (6) assembly, main bearing; (7) screw, main bearing assembly; (8) reed set, main bearing valve; (9) reed stop, main bearing reed valves; (10) washer, reed stop mounting screw; (11) screw, reed stop mounting; (12) piston; (13) piston pin; (14) lock ring, piston pin; (15) ring, piston; (16) connecting rod and cap; (17) screw, connecting rod; (18) nut, connecting rod; (19) needle roller, crankpin; (20) needle roller, piston pin; (21) washer, needle locating.

be tight spots and free spots in each complete rotation of the flywheel. Evidence of this would indicate a bent or twisted crankshaft. Excessive bearing wear most times will be detected by a sloppy feel to the assembly when the flywheel is rotated. By gripping the flywheel on either side and rotating it forward and backward, worn crankshaft journals or (10) excessive connecting rod bearing clearances will be apparent by a sloppy and jerky rather than smooth-sweeping motion of the pistons.

Knocking may also be caused during flywheel rotation if the magneto heel plates strike the magnets built into the flywheel.

7. A broken crankshaft may not always be apparent. If a crankshaft breaks completely at its top end, the flywheel will be loose and can even be picked off the crankcase by hand. However, a crankshaft also may break at some point within the crankcase. The engine may still operate and yet have an apparent vibration knock. Only a complete disassembly of the powerhead will reveal this.

However, any knocking sound from within the crankcase calls for a teardown of the assembly for full inspection of the component parts.

8–9. A bent or twisted connecting rod or bent connecting rod wrist pin may occur for several reasons. The most frequent cause is due to an engine taking in water while still operating at high speed. This usually happens when a moving boat is overturned. Another common type of damage to connecting rods or wrist pins occurs when the propeller, while rotating at high speed, strikes a solid object. Though most manufacturers advertise slip-type clutches, shear rubber propeller hub inserts, or shear pins as propeller protection, these propeller shock-absorbing devices are in essence designed for powerhead protection since they free the reciprocating and rotating powerhead parts from undue strain that would be caused if the propeller shaft were suddenly to cease rotating when a propeller struck a solid object. Some outboard owners of engines equipped with soft shear pins have replaced the soft metal drive pins with hard steel pins to overcome the annoyance of replacing sheared pins. This is not a recommended practice. No pleasure outboarder should adopt any such substitution, for it destroys the protection once given to the powerhead parts.

A loose or bent wrist pin can cause motor knocking. It should be replaced because it produces sloppy motion, leading to an erratic take-up on thrust between connecting rod and piston.

11. Connecting rod end caps seldom become misaligned during operation if they have once been properly aligned. However, these caps usually are mated, and during a major repair job they may be assembled in a reverse manner so that the bearings do not roll smoothly. Suspect this flaw only if the engine has been torn down recently.

12–14. Cylinder and piston damage usually is accompanied by a noticeable loss of compression. A motor which once resisted starting pull during manual starting and had good compression bounce suddenly may become easier to pull over. This indicates a compression loss or blow-by past the piston when it is moving up on compression stroke. Worn piston rings alone may cause this. However, if either the cylinder or piston is badly scored, excessive compression losses will be noticeable. Piston and piston ring scoring may be due to hard flakes of carbon, sand, and grit or broken piston rings. In any event, when there is a compression loss, the cylinders should be removed for inspection.

15. Excessive carbon in the head of a cylinder or on the crown of a piston or both may cause preignition, leading to knocking. This occurs when the carbon is ignited during combustion and continues to glow after combustion of fuel vapor has ceased. This results in firing the fresh charge of induced fuel vapor before the spark is produced by the spark plug in proper time sequence. The carbon may be removed with a solvent or degreasing agent. Hard particles of carbon that don't dissolve may be scraped away from the crown of the piston with a blunt flat object like a putty knife.

Many outboard motors are fitted with intake bypass ports. The covers of these ports may be easily removed so that the condition of pistons and particularly piston rings and ring grooves may be examined without necessitating a complete engine teardown. One test to check for struck or broken piston rings is to remove the port covers, rotate the flywheel until the rings line up in front of the ports, then press on the rings with the blade of a screwdriver. Rings should be springy feeling as the rings are depressed, and then under their spring tension, move out again to cling to the cylinder walls. If the

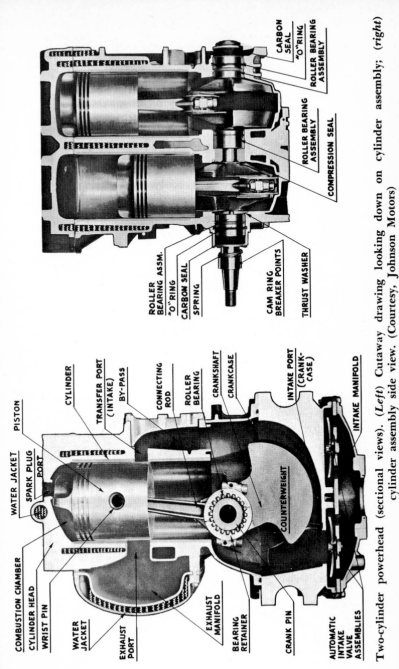

Two-cylinder powerhead (sectional views). (*Left*) Cutaway drawing looking down on cylinder assembly; (*right*) cylinder assembly side view. (Courtesy, Johnson Motors)

Left view labels:

COMBUSTION CHAMBER
CYLINDER HEAD
WRIST PIN
WATER JACKET
EXHAUST PORT
BEARING RETAINER
CRANK PIN
AUTOMATIC INTAKE VALVE ASSEMBLIES

WATER JACKET
SPARK PLUG PORT
PISTON
CYLINDER
TRANSFER PORT (INTAKE)
BY-PASS
CONNECTING ROD
ROLLER BEARING
CRANKSHAFT
CRANKCASE
INTAKE PORT (CRANKCASE)
INTAKE MANIFOLD
EXHAUST MANIFOLD
COUNTERWEIGHT

Right view labels:

ROLLER BEARING ASSM.
"O" RING
CARBON SEAL
SPRING
CAM RING BREAKER POINTS
THRUST WASHER
COMPRESSION SEAL
ROLLER BEARING ASSEMBLY
CARBON SEAL
"O" RING
ROLLER BEARING ASSEMBLY

rings do not move under pressure, they should be suspected either of being stuck or broken. In either case, the cylinder should be removed and piston and rings should be checked.

If an engine while operating suddenly starts to knock badly:

POSSIBLE CAUSE:

1. Overheating.

REMEDY:

1. Immediately stop the engine before it seizes and causes extensive internal damage. Check the water intake of the lower unit. Weeds and debris may have clogged this inlet, preventing the proper flow of water.

Water pumps in the outboard motor are frequently of the impeller type with flexible neoprene impeller blades. A sudden breakdown of the water pump is a rarity. More often sand and silt being pumped through the system will gradually wear away the impeller blades, gradually reducing efficiency of the pump. Only if a motor starts gradually to overheat would wearing of the water pump impeller blades be suspected.

However, all motors are fitted with telltale water bleed holes, usually just below the base of the powerhead in the lower unit exhaust housing. Check these bleed holes when getting underway and if overheating occurs. Failure of water to be expelled through these holes will indicate a water pump failure or cooling system blockage.

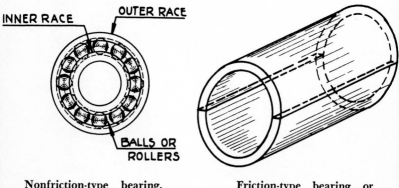

Nonfriction-type bearing. (Courtesy, Johnson Motors)

Friction-type bearing or bronze bushing. (Courtesy, Johnson Motors)

If your motor becomes hard to start, has poor acceleration, shows a decided loss of power and will not idle or idles erratically:

POSSIBLE CAUSES:

1. Compression loss due to items covered under engine noises relating to piston and cylinder condition.

2. Blown or torn gaskets or loose crankcase cylinder head retaining bolts.

3. Water seepage into cylinders due to damaged gaskets or warped mating metal faces.

4. Insufficient oil in fuel mixture.

REMEDIES:

1. With spark plugs removed, a compression gauge check should indicate an excessively low compression reading either on one or all cylinders. The least extensive repair called for would be replacement of piston rings. An examination of the condition of the cylinder block's inner walls and the pistons may show scoring or excessive wear.

Once repairs are made, excessive wear can be prevented from recurring by using the proper quality and quantity of lubricant. Your motor's instruction manual will carry recommendations on this.

An excess of revolutions per minute (r.p.m.) above manufacturer's maximum-rated r.p.m. may cause overheating, leading to scoring and excessive wear. A proper propeller selection will prevent over-revving.

2. Telltale signs of fuel around gaskets usually will reveal leakage. Check the studs or retaining screws for tightness. If they are not tight, tightening them will probably remedy the problem. If they are already tight and the leakage continues, this is a sign of blown, torn, or improperly installed gaskets which must be replaced.

3. Inspect spark plugs for signs of water on the ceramic or electrodes. A small amount of water leaking into the cylinders usually will cause uneven idling characteristics. An excess of water seeping into the cylinders can cause extensive damage. If you have any reason to suspect damaged water jacket gasketing, replace the gaskets. Since excessive water leakage can create uneven cooling, water jacketing heads may warp and must be refaced to prevent a repetition.

4. Every outboarder should pay particular attention to lubrication. Be consistent in preparing fuel-oil mixtures. Always use a top-quality lubricant blended specifically for two-cycle use.

Poor quality oils lead to excessive carbon accumulations in the cylinders and in the exhaust passages. It is unwise to use a detergent-type oil designed to clean the interior of engines. If your motor already has a considerable accumulation of carbon and hard lacquer deposits, the detergent oil will no doubt be successful in softening and relieving the motor of these deposits, but in the process hard carbon particles may be freed and may score cylinder walls and pistons.

If your motor fails to start or backfires when you try to start it:

POSSIBLE CAUSES:

1. Reversed spark plug wires.
2. Broken or damaged reed or inlet valves.

REMEDIES:

1. Manufacturers usually mark the high-tension spark plug lead wires for their proper position. If plug wires are reversed on an alternate firing cylinder engine of two-cylinder design, the spark will be induced 180 degrees out of phase, causing backfiring. Change the wires.

Backfiring, however, also can be caused by malfunctioning valves, by an overly lean air-fuel mixture, or improper ignition timing.

2. Broken or improperly seating reed or leaf valves fail to seal the crankcase so that only partial charges of fuel-air vapor reach the combustion chamber of the cylinders. Broken valves can be detected by fuel spitting back through the carburetor air intake. This indicates almost complete loss of crankcase compression and can only be remedied by replacing the damaged or broken reeds. Occasionally, however, a bit of carbon may wedge under the reed assembly so that it will not fully close. This causes crankcase compression leak. If the foreign matter cannot be displaced by repeated rotation of the flywheel and crankshaft assembly, a motor teardown is required in order to clean and reseat the valves properly.

At times it is impossible to pinpoint operating problems because certain conditions produce similar erratic motor performance. For example, some outboard motor operators have

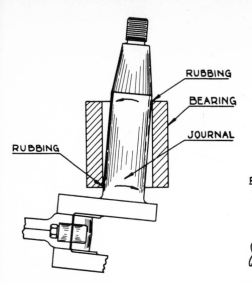

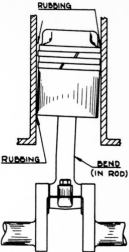

(*Left*) Illustrating condition created by a bent or sprung crankshaft. (Courtesy, Johnson Motors)

(*Right*) Illustrating conditions created by a bent or twisted connecting rod. (Courtesy, Johnson Motors)

had the experience of running at full throttle, having the motor slow down, and, after operating at slower speed, the motor may pick up again and repeat this slow-down-speed-up performance.

The most probable cause of this is a spark plug of an overly hot range (see Chapter 5). If the spark plug is overly hot, the slowdown is caused by the engine reaching a preignition point. The reduction in r.p.m. when the engine slows down allows the plug to return to a normal operating heat range, and the engine will pick up again only to slow again when the preignition occurs. The correction for this, of course, is to replace the faulty plugs with a set of the proper heat range.

A similar reaction is caused by a bent crankshaft or bent or twisted connecting rods which produce a nearly identical result, since the erratic motion created by the faulty parts produces excessive heat. Once the engine has reached a heat range sufficient to expand bearing surfaces, the motor will slow down, and, in slowing down, the parts gradually will cool, allowing the motor the freedom to rev up again.

To further complicate the troubleshooting of this type of erratic action, dirt in the fuel line can cause a motor to starve, and the motor will slow down. Once having slowed down, suction will be reduced, fuel will flow freely, the motor will speed up, suction will increase, and the increased suction will cause another obstruction in the fuel line.

A variation of this occurs in a vapor lock. The fuel supply line, perhaps through proximity to the exhaust passages or due to motor operation under excessively hot temperature or engine temperature raised due to a clogged or partially clogged cooling system, will create fuel boiling or vapor lock. The motor will starve for want of fuel, r.p.m. will drop, the engine will cool, the fuel will stop boiling, and the speed-up-slow-down process will keep repeating.

The best precaution against any powerhead failure is to have a thorough check of all powerhead components at least once an operating season. As soon as any abnormal noise or operating characteristic develops, troubleshoot the engine to find the cause. Repairs made soon enough will minimize the likelihood of more extensive damage.

7. Lower Unit Maintenance and Troubleshooting

The outboard motor lower unit is made up of the transom clamp bracket, the drive-shaft housing, gear case, plus the necessary shafting and gearing to carry crankshaft power to the propeller shaft. The lower unit also houses a means to transfer a flow of raw water to the cylinder block, plus a means to dispose of exhaust gases underwater.

Lower units are broken down into several categories. The nonshift type is found on most engines of older design and still retained on some of the smallest models of each manufacturer's line.

The nonshift type usually incorporates a 360-degree reversing feature, actually nothing more than a complete 360-degree pivot of powerhead and lower unit. Though the clamp bracket remains fixed, the balance of the motor is free to pivot so that the propeller, normally thrusting from the rear of the gear case toward the transom of the boat to impart forward motion, is reversed so the propeller's thrust is astern.

The neutral clutch models are the second type. These motors can be started in neutral and shifted into forward gear, but they do not offer any reverse gear. Some neutral-forward designs provide for reversing with the 360-degree pivoting arrangement. Others have no reversing feature.

The most common gearshift models include forward, neutral, and reverse shifting. Another type of shift mechanism, the complete reversing power type, was described in Chapter 1.

Most lower unit troubles can be attributed to neglect or abuse. With a minimum of care and proper operational practices, the lower unit should be trouble free for the entire life of the motor.

The most frequent abuse leading to trouble is the failure of outboard motor owners to keep a constant check on the lower unit lubricant level. The lower unit lubricant reduces friction in lower unit gears and the bearings supporting the propeller shaft. The lubricant also serves as an aid to the grease seal to prevent the entry of water into the gear case and provides a film over all the metal parts to protect them from rust and corrosion. However, in time, wear between rotating parts gradually will reduce sealing ability. Water will then enter the gear housing and force the lubricant either up through the drive-shaft housing or out through the propeller end of the gearbox where the propeller shaft is supported.

Though water in itself serves as a good lubricant, it will not protect the internal parts of the unit from rust and corrosion. For this reason, it is necessary that the lubricant level of the unit be checked continually.

Another abuse is the improper care of lower units when the motor is not in use. If a motor is to be stored on a boat, the motor should be tilted upward and locked in a positive tilt position so that the unit is free of the water. This applies both to salt- and fresh-water storage. Though salt water will cause much more rapid deterioration, fresh water frequently contains impurities that attack and corrode or pit the aluminum alloy castings of which the gear case housing is constructed.

Care should be taken in storage and in transporting the engine to keep the lower unit at a slightly lower level than the powerhead. If not, water in the lower unit can flow into the exhaust passages and reach the piston and crankcase assemblies

Four months of improper in-the-water storage created this fantastic marine growth condition on boat and motor.

causing powerhead components to rust. Motors stored in unheated locations in freezing weather should be thoroughly drained of all water in the cooling system. If this is not done, freezing may rupture any parts still containing water, such as block assembly, gear case or coolant transfer tubes, and water passages within aluminum castings.

Carelessness in operating an outboard motor in shallow rocky or sandy water can cause undue wear and severe damage to the lower unit. The operator should be careful to tilt up the motor when beaching a boat rather than driving the boat under power onto a beach. Silt and sand-filled water will not only mar the exterior of the skeg and gear case but may clog or break the water pump or clog the water coolant passages, causing the motor to overheat and ultimately seize.

All outboard motors are equipped with some telltale means to determine whether or not the motor is pumping water. These are usually small water bleed holes on the drive-shaft housing above the water line, or bleed tubes extending from the top of the drive-shaft housing. The outboard motor operator should adopt the habit of checking these water relief outlets or have someone check the outlets when getting underway to be sure that the motor is pumping water. At slow speed and idling, a fine mist of water will be expelled. A steady stream will be apparent at high speed.

Close-up view of the propeller shaft, gears, and bearing surfaces found in lower unit of a large horsepower outboard motor. (Courtesy, Johnson Motors)

It is recommended that after any prolonged operation of the motor in shallow water where mud and small foreign particles may have been pumped through the cooling system, or after each salt-water operation, that the motor be flushed with fresh water. If the motor is a small model, it can be removed from the boat and put into a tub of water and run for a few minutes. If a neutral is provided, operate the motor in neutral. Many of the larger motors incorporate a special flushing fitting to which a garden hose can be attached. Should it not be possible to flush the interior cooling passages with fresh water, it is still a good idea to pour a bucket of fresh water over the outside of the lower unit to prevent exterior housing corrosion. This sounds like a lot of trouble and it is, but it will pay off in longer life of the unit.

Older style outboard motors largely depended on a combination pressure siphon-vacuum circulating method for cooling. A water scoop usually was located on the forward side of the trailing edge of the lower unit just under the anticavitation plate. The whirling of the propeller forced a stream of water through the water scoop and circulated it through tubes inside the unit, integral to the housing castings, or along the outside of the lower unit housing to the circulating passages surrounding the cylinders. At high speeds, this method was quite efficient. At slow or trolling speeds, however, pressure of the water thrown from the tips of the propeller blades was seldom sufficient to cause proper circulation. The design theory was that once circulation started, a siphoning action of having a

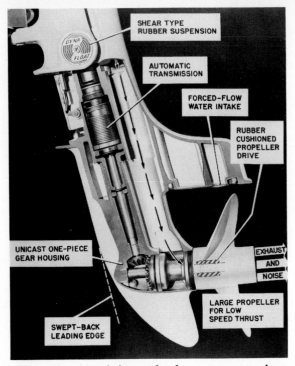

Automatic transmission and other components in a midrange horsepower outboard motor. (Courtesy, Mercury Motors)

water discharge below the intake would keep the circulation constant. However, the siphoning or suction action depended on completely airtight water lines. Any leak anywhere in the system would weaken or destroy the flow. Overheating would result and many of the older-type outboard motors suffered bearing, piston, and cylinder damage due to inefficient cooling during excessive slow-speed operation.

Contemporary outboard motors are with few exceptions cooled by water circulation provided by a positive-type water pump. The most commonplace type uses flexible neoprene impeller blades which are fairly trouble free. However, continued operation in water containing a large quantity of silt or sand eventually will result in enlargement of the pump casing, reduction in size of the flexible impeller blades, and loss of pumping action.

The pump casings in some outboard motors are not designed for continual use in salt-water operation unless they are flushed with fresh water following use. On some models of motors manufactured about the mid-1950's, manufacturers offer as an optional extra stainless-steel water-pump casing replacements. These casings will withstand far more abuse of operation in sand- and silt-filled water.

Should you buy a secondhand motor which has been run extensively in salt water, insist on a replacement of the water pump by one suitable for salt-water use or a written guarantee for replacement of any damaged parts plus the labor required for such replacement should the motor be damaged due to improper cooling.

Other ways to provide water circulation are by means of plunger and vane assembly pumps. The plunger type is composed of a plunger located within a cylinder which is operated by a cam or an eccentric located on the propeller shaft. A spring maintains pressure on the plunger which in turn is forced in and out by the cam riding against one end of the plunger. Poppet or ball-check valves control the water flow. The sliding vane design of pump is operated, too, by a cam on the propeller shaft or lower section of the drive shaft.

When no telltale stream or mist of water is apparent and overheating occurs:

POSSIBLE CAUSES:

1. Partially clogged or obstructed water inlet.
2. Weak or broken spring on plunger-type pump.
3. Faulty check valve on plunger-type pump.
4. Worn rubber rotor vanes or impeller improperly fitted to eccentric on shaft.
5. Worn or broken cam on sliding vane or plunger pump.
6. Clogged water tubes or clogged water jacket in cylinders.
7. Faulty lower unit grease seal, permitting gear lubricant to interfere with operation of check valves, impeller, sliding vane, plunger, or spring assembly in the latter.

REMEDIES:

1. Clean away marine growth, weeds, or any other obstacles obstructing water inlet.
2–7. Have cooling system checked by a skilled outboard motor repairman.

If the factory finish of the lower unit castings has been properly maintained and not nicked or worn by running and dragging through sand, the metal will withstand considerable salt-water service without deterioration. The alloy used in the modern outboard motor has been carefully chosen for corrosion resistance, has then been given a chemical treatment, and sprayed with a salt-water resistant primer and finish coat. Yet none of these corrosion preventives will be of any value once the unit has been badly scarred and scuffed. Because of this, it is strongly suggested that periodically you inspect the finish of the lower unit, touch up marred surface areas with a lower unit spray paint of the aerosol, pressure-can type carried by all outboard motor dealers.

Your gearshift controls will to a great extent determine the life of the gears and the shifting mechanism. Nearly all modern outboard shift-type motors are provided with an overspeed neutral stop or detent position so that gear shifting cannot be done at excessive r.p.m. Should your motor not have such an overspeed stop, make a practice of shifting at moderate speed only.

Your shifts should be made with a positive forceful movement. The slow timid shift does not permit the gears to mesh positively but rather allows the tips of the gears to come in contact at their tapered tips so that chipping or stripping of the gears will result.

A competent outboard operator is familiar with the sound of his motor's operation. New and strange noises serve as a warning.

If you note any unusual noises that seem to come from the gear housing:

POSSIBLE CAUSES:
1. Propeller shaft worn or sprung.
2. Broken or chipped propeller or pinion gears.
3. Worn bearings.
4. Propeller hub striking gear case cover.
5. Improperly fitted gears.
6. No grease in gear housing.

Various components in a conventional neutral-forward-reverse shifting two-cycle outboard motor. (Courtesy, Evinrude Motors)

DRIVE PINION BEARING
DRIVE PINION
CLUTCH DOG SHIFTER
PROPELLER SHAFT BEARING (FRONT)
LOWER GEAR CASE ATTACHING SCREW
GEAR CASE DRAIN SCREW
GEAR CASE (LOWER)
PROPELLER SHAFT GEARS
SHIFTER LEVER
GEAR CASE SKEG

REVERSE LOCK
INLET WATER TUBE
FLUSHING PLUG
SHIFT ROD (LOWER)

RUNNING MOTOR IN TEST TANK

WHEN RUNNING A BIG TWIN IN A TEST TANK, BE
SURE TO REMOVE UPPER BYPASS COVER ON THE
GEAR CASE. THIS IS THE SMALL METAL STRIP ON
THE PORT SIDE OF THE GEAR HOUSING JUST ABOVE
THE CAVITATION PLATE. THIS ALLOWS THE MOTOR
TO TAKE IN SUFFICIENT WATER TO COOL PROPERLY.

EXHAUST OUTLET
WATER INLET SCREEN
WATER INLET PLUG
WATER INLET
PROPELLER
PROPELLER NUT
PROPELLER SHAFT
PROPELLER SHAFT SEAL
PROPELLER SHAFT BALL BEARING (REAR)

73

REMEDIES:

Any deficiency of the gear housing, other than the lack of lubricant, will require a replacement or adjustment by a skilled mechanic.

Aside from neglect, lack of lubricant may be caused by carelessness in replacing the drain or inspection plug so that vibration loosens it, or the lack may be due to a defective oil or grease seal which will call for replacement.

Many motors use a shear-pin drive to make a positive linkage between propeller shaft and propeller. The shear pin serves two purposes. It offers some protection to the propeller should you strike an underwater obstacle or a floating object, but more important, the shear pin also offers protection to other parts of the motor. Propellers are relatively inexpensive to replace and their replacement is simply accomplished. A broken crankshaft, drive shaft, prop shaft, gears, and other components are far more costly and require extensive labor to replace. Remember, the shear pin protects these parts.

Because of this, it must be stressed again that you should not be tempted to replace the soft brass drive or shear pins with hard steel pins so as not to have the annoyance of replacing shear pins. With a steel pin replacement, extensive damage can occur if the propeller should strike an obstacle that does not give on impact. The propeller not only would be destroyed, but the strain on internal parts would be almost certain to cause additional damage.

Most of the newer model outboard motors are fitted with propellers containing rubber inserts in the hubs. Under stress, the rubber will twist or rotate to relieve strain on power train parts.

Operators of some outboard motors have replaced relatively lightweight aluminum propellers with heavier bronze props. This added weight creates inertia during acceleration and may be the cause of frequent shear-pin breakage. On motors that do not incorporate a shear-pin feature but have instead slip clutches or special shock absorber hubs in the original factory propellers, replacement propellers of the wrong type may cause damage to gear teeth or other components because of the propeller's added weight. Though a selection of propellers is recommended for most outboard motors (see Chapter 12, "Propeller Selection and Care"), replacement propellers should be used only after consulting with your outboard motor dealer so as to be sure that the replacement propellers will not only be more efficient than the factory-supplied average propeller, but will also be compatible to the design of the motor in regard to shifting, acceleration, and protection of drive train parts.

8. Care of the Electric-Starting System

Electric-starting outboard motors have had a revolutionary effect on outboard motorboating. Along with the added convenience of remote gearshift and throttle controls, electric starters have made it possible for outboard motors to be installed on large hulls in the 20′ and over category.

Most of the larger outboard motors are now either equipped with electric starters, or the electric starters are available as alternate optional equipment. The installations have proved to be quite trouble free, and it isn't necessary for the present-day outboarder to be an electrician in order to keep his electric starter and remote electrical accessory equipment in top-notch operating condition.

The key to reliability and the heart of the system is a storage battery of adequate capacity maintained in a charged condition. The outboard motor battery usually is sold as a separate accessory item. It's a false economy to cut budget corners by buying a cheap battery.

Each manufacturer in his maintenance manual recommends the minimum capacity battery required to operate the electric starter and normally used electrical accessory items. In general, the recommendation is for a battery of a 50-ampere-hour capacity or more. A variation of this recommendation is for the motor manufacturer to specify the selection of a battery with a capacity offering a certain minimum operational time at a specified continuous ampere rate of discharge. An example of this is a battery with a cold starting capacity of a minimum of $5\frac{1}{2}$ minutes at a continuous 150-ampere rate of discharge.

If these specifications are foreign to you, toss the problem into the lap of your dealer who should know. Be sure that the guarantee that accompanies the battery specifies the factory-recommended minimum output or more.

MAGNETO-ALTERNATOR PROVIDES POWER
TO DRIVE A. C. EQUIPMENT
THROUGH THESE LEADS

IGNITION AND GENERATING LEADS
ARE SMALL WIRES CAPABLE OF BEING FLEXED
THROUGH MOVEMENT OF STATOR

RECTIFIER

SHORT, HI-TENSION LEADS

SPEED-CONTROLLING STATOR CARRIES
1 LOW-TENSION IGNITION COIL,
3 GENERATING COILS,
AND 2 SETS OF BREAKER POINTS

HI-TENSION COILS

MAGNETO-ALTERNATOR PROVIDES
D. C. FOR BATTERY, LIGHTS,
AND OTHER EQUIPMENT
THROUGH THIS LEAD

AMP. QUICK-DISCONNECT, COVERED TERMINALS
FOR SIMPLE SERVICE AND PROTECTION

Generators provided on most two-cycle outboard motors are of
the alternator-rectifier type, as on this Oliver two-cylinder motor.

Few electric-starting failures are attributable to major equipment breakdowns. The troubles are far more likely to be
caused by minor faults, easily corrected, and avoidable with
proper maintenance.

*When the starter key or press button is operated and the
motor's starter fails to turn the motor over or turns it over too
slowly to start:*

POSSIBLE CAUSES:

1. Discharged battery.
2. Faulty contact at battery terminal.
3. Faulty contact at starter solenoid.
4. Faulty contact at starter motor.

REMEDIES:

1. All batteries are subject to self-discharge when not in use.
The only remedy for a discharged battery is to recharge or
replace the battery. Since a low battery is the most frequent
cause of electric-starting failures, here are some tips on proper
battery maintenance.

Most batteries will offer a hundred or more starts without
battery failure even though the motor is not equipped with a
generator to rejuvenate the used-up charge. It can be truly

Exposed front view of electric-starting Mercury outboard motor showing starter motor at upper left. Note that on this type of engine two sets of starter gears are used since engine is a complete reversing type.

said that more batteries are killed by their owners than die of natural discharge causes. Battery death is due either to complete or partial neglect, complete starvation, faulty diet, or being beaten.

The ordinary storage battery consists of a group of individual cells, each containing a series of lead peroxide plates, separated by a porous reinforcing material. A dilute solution of sulfuric acid covering these plates reacts chemically when an electrical resistance, such as that caused by the operation of a starter or the use of electrical accessories, is placed on the plates. This chemical reaction progressively discharges the battery.

The reverse reaction occurs when current is fed back to the battery from an outboard motor's generator. Gradually, as the chemical reaction continues, with the alternate discharg-

Showing location of a 12-volt starter motor as used in Evinrude 35-horsepower models.

ing and charging, the life of the battery is expended as the plates slowly erode. However, the battery life can be prolonged if it is given proper care. The electrolyte solution formed by the addition of water to the dilute sulfuric acid should be maintained at a level of $\frac{1}{8}''$ to $\frac{1}{4}''$ above the plates. Permitting the plates to be exposed leads to warping of the plates and separators and rapid decomposition. The battery itself should be maintained in clean condition with the terminal posts kept free of corrosion. The battery's filler cap vent holes should not be allowed to be clogged, for gases formed by the chemical reaction occurring within the battery must be allowed to escape.

The battery should be kept on a liquid diet of uncontaminated water—distilled water is recommended. Any foreign metallic content in the water used to maintain electrolyte level may cause a contamination and lead to shorting and rapid dissipation of the plates, reducing battery life. If the battery is given too much water, the electrolyte solution may become too dilute and the battery acid is likely to slosh out of the filler cap breather holes, causing acid contamination of the top of the battery. This would lead to the destruction of the terminal posts and the battery cables.

Avoid special patented "rejuvenators." The Association of American Battery Manufacturers specifically warns against the addition of any of the patented chemical solutions. The AABM states that the use of chemical rejuvenators will cause a rapid shortening of battery life and will void manufacturer's guarantees.

Care should be taken to install junction box securely and in a protected position. Loose wires or the entry of salt water can cause starting trouble.

Self-discharge of batteries increases rapidly with any increase in temperature. A battery that will maintain a charge when not in use for 2½ months at 60 degrees F. may be completely discharged within 15 days' time at 100 degrees temperature. Store your battery in a protected area. See, too, that it is properly secured so that hull vibrations and the pounding action of waves do not damage it. Most marine dealers carry specially designed battery securing pads, straps, or boxes.

Be particularly careful about where the battery is located. Don't secure it in a transom well just forward of a motor or the battery may be crushed should the motor tilt up.

List among your required tools for motor maintenance a hydrometer. Most hydrometers are set to give accurate readings at 80 degrees F. Compensation for temperature variance is very simple. For each 10 degrees below 80 degrees F., subtract .004 from the reading. For each 10 degrees above standard, add .004 to the reading. In general, the specific gravity of acid water solution is 1.280 and a fully charged battery will show a specific gravity reading of 1.280. Recently some heavy-duty batteries have been filled with an electrolyte rated at a specific gravity of 1.260. You may safely assume that electrolyte of the former specific gravity has been used unless your battery is plainly marked that it contains a 1.260 solution.

Application of petroleum jelly to battery terminals will
help offset accumulation of corrosion.

A battery charged three-quarters will give a reading of
1.220. At half-charge the hydrometer reading is 1.160. If the
hydrometer indicates 1.150 or less, the battery should be recharged before you go boating or be replaced with a new battery, for there probably will not be enough current available
to operate the starter.

2–4. Remove the clamps from the battery terminals, scrape
clamps and terminals clean with a screwdriver or knife blade,
and replace clamps tightly. If the terminals are checked while
you are still at a mooring and you have access to waterproof
grease or petroleum jelly, it is recommended that you coat
the terminals and contact leads to prevent the accumulation
of corrosion.

Check wiring for loose, broken, or corroded contacts at the
starter solenoid and at the starter motor.

Since the outboard boat is subject to far more vibration than
the electric-starting system of an automobile, it is possible
for connectors to work loose. The weight of the heavy wiring
harness cables, if improperly supported, can also lead to broken

contacts. In salt-water operation particularly, it is possible for the starting switch mechanism to become corroded. Failure to make a complete circuit may be traced to this point.

When the starter motor rotates the flywheel, yet the motor does not start:

Check for a faulty electrically operated choke mechanism. Naturally, too, any of the starting failures enumerated in earlier chapters may also apply.

Some motors are equipped with manual as well as electrically energized choke mechanisms. If your motor is fitted with a manual choke, try this while one of your passengers operates the starter switch button. If the motor starts readily under manual choke, the fault lies with the electrically energized choke mechanism—probably with the choke solenoid.

If the starter motor spins freely, but the motor does not turn over:

POSSIBLE CAUSE:

1. Starter gear or flywheel gears are not engaging due to excessive wear or improper positioning of starter on powerhead.

REMEDY:

1. Worn or damaged gears will require adjustment or replacement by a skilled mechanic.

If starter motor is loose on its mountings, tighten the securing hardware and try starting again. If starter pinion gear and flywheel gear still fail to engage, the electric-starting system should be repaired by a skilled mechanic.

Fires due to faulty electric-starting systems are a rarity. However, considerable damage may be done to the electric-starting system if wires in the wiring harness overheat.

If smoke or excessive heat is noted in the electric-starting system:

POSSIBLE CAUSES:

1. Short circuit in the wiring system.
2. Reversed or improperly connected battery terminals.
3. Short circuit in starter solenoid.
4. Short circuit in starter motor.

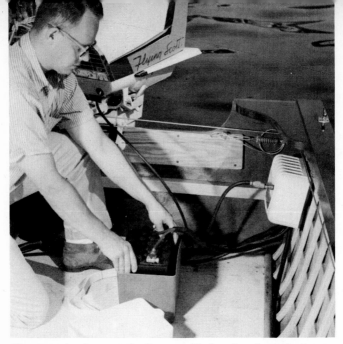

Constant jarring can lead to rapid deterioration of storage batteries on small boats. Batteries should be housed in a specially designed container, then properly secured.

REMEDIES:

1. Inspect all wiring for frayed insulation or broken wires, touching adjacent wires or grounding to powerhead. Tighten or repair any wiring faults.

2. Reverse leads from battery terminals, being certain that the positive and negative terminals are connected to the proper leads, at least one of which will be marked.

3. The starter solenoid is an automatic switch mechanism. When the starter key is turned, the solenoid automatically completes contact so that current reaches the starter motor. The starter solenoid body will become warm if it is shorted. If no exterior wiring faults are noted and solenoid is overheating, an internal short is indicated. The solenoid should be tested by the dealer and repaired or replaced if defective.

4. If the starter motor itself is overheating, this may be due to a bearing failure in the motor's drive shaft or to an internal short. In any event, disconnect the starting switch until the system has been checked over by an expert.

Most electric-starting motors may be started manually. However, a word of caution—the wiring arrangement of each model of outboard motor will be unique to that model or series of one basic design. Study your operating manual carefully. Very probably it will be necessary for the electric-starting switch to be placed at an "on" position before the motor will start. However, in order not to damage further the electric-starting system, varying models of motors may require certain elements of the electric-starting system to be disconnected before operating the power plant without a battery connected to the engine.

Remember that the miscellaneous accessories, such as running lights, radio, and horn, all place a drain on the battery. Some outboard motors are fitted with generators. Others are not. Those with generators have a varying output of 5 to 25 or more amperes. Some offer full generator output at a modest operating r.p.m. Others produce their full output only at or near peak r.p.m. This has an effect on the amount of current you may safely draw without danger of discharging your battery.

Check the amperage requirement of your accessories or have your dealer do it for you. Then learn to budget your amperes, if operation of all accessories simultaneously should appear to be excessive.

9. Maintenance of Remote Controls

Under the general category of remote controls fall all of those items which permit the operator to helm his boat at a location remote from the powerhead. Not too many years ago all outboard motors were controlled by levers, buttons, knobs, and toggles located on the front of the powerhead. Steering was by tiller bar, which in some instances incorporated the further refinements of shift mechanism or speed control in a twist-grip-type handle. All but the most modest sized outboard motors today are steered by an automotive-type steering wheel with shift and throttle control mechanism either combined in a single lever or two separate levers located within easy reach of the operator.

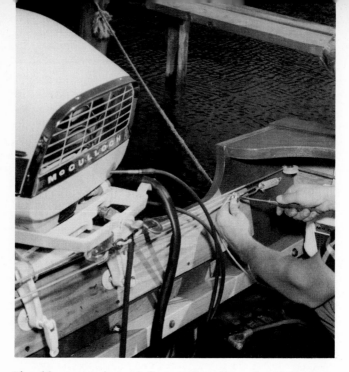

If cable system is used for steering, lines should be kept
taut and securing hardware should be checked periodically.
(Courtesy, Scott Motors)

However, as long as the outboard motor and the boat are
sold as separate units and manufactured independently of one
another, boat, motor, and controls will not be wholly mated.
Problems will arise in trying to achieve smooth functioning
of remote controls, and maintenance problems will exist.

No real troubleshooting is involved in analyzing shift or
throttle or steering problems with a conventional push-pull,
bowdoin cable type, throttle-shift controls and pulley-cable
steering arrangements. The traditional pulley-cable steering is
trouble free if the initial installation is adequate and the hardware and accessories are of first quality. Problems with cable
steering usually can be attributed to cheap pulleys which permit cables to bind; guides with overly small eyes for the
diameter of the cable, leading to binding and chafing; pulleys
and guides improperly located; or cables not properly wound
on the steering wheel drum.

Too much slack in the cable lines will cause erratic steering and may create a dangerous handling characteristic. Slack can be eliminated from lines by the insertion of a heavy-duty steering cable spring. Such springs are designed specifically to take up slack and are stocked by all marine dealers. Larger pulley sheaves with swivel mounts will prevent cables from slipping out of the pulleys.

However, the boatman may well want to improve on his present steering. Accessories firms in recent years have designed many handy modifications, and it would be worth any new boatman's time or that of any boatman refitting his boat to check some of the latest steering items. For example, there are steering wheels with mounting brackets that pivot to any angle from 0 to nearly 45 degrees and offer adjustable shaft lengths. The use of such a wheel can convert an uncomfortable steering position to a relaxing helming spot.

Another innovation is a special drum mounted on a conventional steering wheel. The drum utilizes a bidirectional Novak clutch. This is the type of clutch that long has been used in aircraft to retain deflection angles in wing flaps and other aircraft movable control surfaces and submarine control surfaces. The unique wheel offers a finger-light touch, yet the operator can remove his hands from the steering wheel without the steering angle being changed by wave deflection or motor torque.

There are also a number of mechanical, hydraulic, and electrohydraulic steering systems on the market. One motor manufacturer makes a smooth-functioning mechanical steering system that may be applied to motors of any manufacture.

Nearly all of the major motor manufacturers now offer as standard equipment or accessory equipment single-lever, combination shift and throttle controls. All of these controls add immeasurably to the ease of operation of the outboard motor. Maintenance requirements are lubrication so that corrosion or rust will not cause the controls to freeze and proper adjustment. Adjustments are required so that shifts can be made within a safe r.p.m. range, and the throttle spark advance combination must be adjusted so that, teamed together, controls offer the full operating range offered by the motor. Improperly adjusted controls can restrict top speed or prevent slow idling.

Again we encounter variances in remote-control designs, model for model and manufacturer to manufacturer. Here are some points to check that will apply to most remote controls.

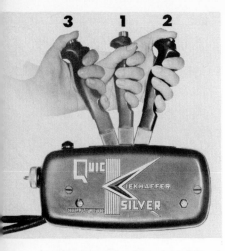

Many larger motors are fitted with single-lever controls so that shift and speed may be handled in one motion. Controls pictured are from full-reversing powerhead-type Mercury motor.

Be sure that the control head mounting is secured snugly to a flat mounting pad. The mounting pad should be located in such a way that the cables do not bind by being forced to bend through too abrupt radii. Uneven or warped mounting pad surfaces can cause a distortion of the control head casting or cause the control lever to bind when the mounting screws are tightened. Sometimes a slight shimming of the mounting bolts with washers will level the control so that it operates smoothly.

Within the control head will be located some form of gear train or cam mechanism. A light coating of waterproof grease should be placed on metal gear trains or pivot shafts to protect them from rust or corrosion. If your boat operates in a salt-water area, from time to time the control head should be taken apart and the moving and mating parts within should be cleaned of any foreign accumulations, corrosion, and rust, and then a light coating of waterproof grease placed on the parts.

The housing studs on some designs must be kept secured. If the two halves of the housing are permitted play, gears may not mesh properly.

The cables should be secured along the sides of the boat, but clamps should not be drawn up excessively or binding between the outer sheathing and the inner cable within can result.

Problems sometimes occur in installing or shifting controls from a starboard or portside installation or vice versa. All out-

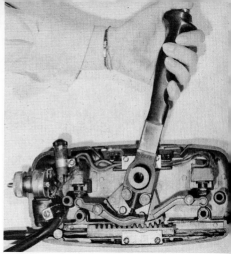

Mercury single-lever control (exposed view) showing electric-starting key switch, choke control, shift lever, and throttle mechanism all functioning within a single housing.

board motors offer some propeller torque that may cause a boat to list or want to list in the direction of the torque force. The direction of the torque force will depend on the direction of rotation of the outboard motor's propeller. This is another feature of outboard motors that varies model for model, as some motors are fitted with right-hand rotating propellers, others with propellers of left-hand rotation.

If you are in doubt as to which side your controls should be placed to offset prop torque, consult with your outboard dealer. Your boat will offer far better straightaway and turning performance if the controls are placed to that side of the boat opposite torque reaction.

Generally speaking, loosely strung cables of greater than minimum length required will offer easier operation of remote controls with less tendency to bind than will cables of bare minimum length. New installations of remote shift and throttle spark advance usually will call for minor adjustments. An inspection of your control linkage will reveal a means to shorten or lengthen the operating stroke of both the shift mechanisms and the throttle controls.

Usually you will find that adjustments to the throttle can be made only when the shift mechanism is in gear. Otherwise an overspeed stop, which is a safety mechanism, will come into play to prevent throttle advance beyond idling.

Some designs of remote-control mechanisms provide for adjustments at the control box as well as at the motor. Again an inspection of your own motor's remote controls will be called for.

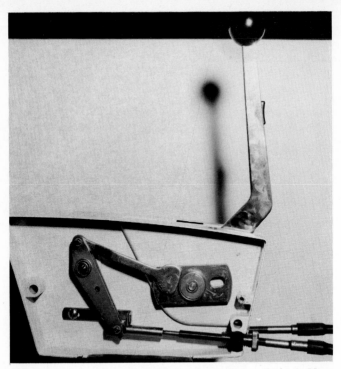

One-half of the Scott single-lever control (exposed view). Note how adjustments can be made with thumb screws located on rear of control box.

Every boatman should plan in advance for emergency breakdown actions. In the event your motor's controls should at any time cause the engine to jam in a full- or partial-speed condition or jam in gear, you should be ready to cope with the situation. With an electric-starting motor you need only turn off the switch and the runaway boat will be brought under control. On another model, you may be able to shift into neutral and step to the rear of the boat and choke out the motor or turn off the control button. Many remote controls are fitted with a toggle switch that will ground out the ignition and stop your motor should an emergency occur. The important thing to remember is never to become rattled; plan in advance for all contingencies. Ability to respond properly to an emergency is the hallmark of the skilled boat handler.

10. The Value of a Tachometer and Speedometer

Only a small minority of outboard motor owners are interested in all-out racing speed. However, a far greater percentage of outboard owners would be interested in speed if they realized that speed has a direct relationship to economy of operation. This can be better understood, perhaps, if an example is given.

Assume that an outboard owner operates a 15' outboard hull powered by a 35-horsepower motor. The manner in which he has set up the motor, its condition of tune and propeller choice gives it a maximum speed of 25 m.p.h. Operating at full throttle at this speed, the engine consumes four gallons of fuel per hour. If the owner were able to increase the maximum speed of the boat to 29 m.p.h., by means of proper tuning, altered motor setup on the boat, or a different propeller selection, he would be adding four more miles for every four gallons of fuel consumed. If within the economy range of the motor, at about three-quarters throttle, the same boat clocked 21 m.p.h., and through proper motor adjustment, tuning, and setup, his cruising speed could be increased to 23 m.p.h., he would still enjoy a more-than-modest fuel saving. If the cruising speed of 21 m.p.h. suited the owner, it would mean that he could reach and maintain this speed at a considerably lesser throttle setting.

So added speed can mean added economy.

Speed on the water, however, is extremely deceptive. Most boatmen are inclined to overrate the speed of their craft. There's no harm to this unless it interferes with navigation or is costly in terms of operational performance.

The weight balance of a boat, particularly in a more modest sized outboard, is extremely critical. The shift of one passenger three or four feet forward or aft from front to rear cockpit may mean the addition in speed of several miles an hour in the 20 m.p.h. to 30 m.p.h. range. This may seem negligible, but if a squall is approaching, the added 2 m.p.h. could mean the difference between reaching a protected harbor or being buffeted about by the storm.

As camp boating, weekend traveling, and cruising by outboard become more popular, the outboard boatman planning to engage in these activities must learn some of the basic

Typical outboard-type tachometer for dashboard mounting. Components are sealed against moisture and vibration. Instrument is extremely helpful in motor setup.

principles of navigation. One of the first things he will learn is that in even the simplest form of piloting, some accurate means to measure his boat's speed must be available to him. At night or in a fog, an error of 10 per cent to 20 per cent resulting from sheer guesswork can stick him high and dry on a mud flat or run his boat onto a reef rather than safely navigating a change of channel direction.

There are two instruments that any outboard owner must have at his command if he is interested in gaining maximum performance from his equipment or engaging in rudimentary piloting and navigation. While either instrument is helpful, neither is complete in itself, since one complements the other. The two instruments are a water speedometer and a tachometer.

Both of these instruments are designed to check speed. One records the boat speed over the surface of the water. The other records the speed performance of the motor in terms of revolutions per minute of the crankshaft.

The water speedometer functions on the basis of water pressure. As boat speed is, for example, doubled, water pressure in the pitot or impact tube, as the pickup commonly mounted on the transom of the boat is termed, is quadrupled. Since this relationship between pressure and speed is a constant one, a Bourdon-type pressure gauge used for water speedometers may be calibrated accurately, and pressure exerted on a diaphragm can be translated into speed.

Two outboard-type water speedometers. Such instruments are quite accurate and help outboarders achieve peak performance from their equipment.

The water impact tube on the outboard boat should be located out of the slip stream or a disturbed water area that may be created by the boat's keel.

Water speedometers for outboard use have been placed on the market at modest prices so that calibrations at all speed ranges may not always be exact. Because of this, it is recommended that any boatowner planning to use his water speedometer as a navigational instrument for determining distance covered versus time of a run should compare his speedometer at varying speeds with stop watch readings through an accurately measured trap. By consulting charts of your local area, you will be able to find accurately measured distances between channel or other markers. Some local outboard clubs have installed surveyed one-half mile or one-mile runs just for speed timing purposes.

The outboarder should also realize that in referring to his water speedometer that the speed indicated is the speed of his boat over the water or through the water and not over the bottom. In general his principal interest will be in speed over the bottom, since this can be translated into distance made good in a given time.

Variation between speed through or over the water and over the bottom will be caused by prevailing current, which can be checked locally or in some instances will be recorded in some form of navigational aids unique to a given area. If you have a water speedometer sensitive in the extreme low ranges, it is possible to anchor, and the speed of the current will be recorded on your water speedometer.

However, inherent to many of the mass-produced, inexpensive, outboard water speedometers is their inaccuracy in ranges below 8 m.p.h. to 10 m.p.h.

However, once you have determined whether your own water speedometer is accurate or inaccurate, you can use it as a reference instrument and for navigation. If it is wholly accurate, you need only add its recording to the velocity of the current if you are running with the current, or subtract the speed of the current from the water speedometer reading if you are bucking the current to determine your true speed over the bottom.

If your water speedometer is inaccurately calibrated and proved as such by a stop watch-timed run through a trap, then you may make up a mathematical compensation chart correcting the readings at various indicated meter speeds.

However, you may use your water speedometer as a tool to aid in tune-up and setup to attain more speed at any given throttle setting by means of changes of propeller, motor mounting height, or engine angle. Improvements in or failure to improve the boat's speed will become immediately apparent, and, since errors will be consistent, the amount of improvement will be measurable even though the instrument may be reading fast or slow.

A tachometer, as we've already said, measures the r.p.m. of the motor's crankshaft. Since the development of horsepower depends on r.p.m., the tachometer is used to determine whether the motor at full throttle is developing the full-rated r.p.m. possible from its design. The tachometer will further serve as an instrument to warn the boatowner whether the motor is being operated at an excessive r.p.m. range where continued operation could cause damage.

It will also indicate when the motor is in need of a tune-up or a general overhaul.

Though as we have pointed out in Chapter 7, "Lower Unit Maintenance and Troubleshooting," only in the case of a limited number of motors intended purely for competition does the propeller rotate at the same number of r.p.m. as the crankshaft. More commonly, the propeller shaft is geared to

The author, using portable tachometer to check condition of tune-up of a motor.

turn considerably more slowly than the motor itself. However, the propeller revolutions and those of the crankshaft are constantly in direct proportion.

At the time a manufacturer's motor is given a horsepower rating, this rating is taken from the motor's crankshaft and is developed at a specified r.p.m.

A glance at any horsepower curve will show that at any point below an engine's rated r.p.m., the engine no longer develops its full horsepower. Because of this the boat owner, whose motor is not capable of turning up to its full-rated r.p.m. due to either the condition of tuning, the setup on the boat, or improper propeller selection, receives only a fraction of the horsepower he paid for.

As an example of this, one manufacturer's 40-horsepower motor develops its full horsepower at 4,800 r.p.m. Assume the motor at the time it is bought is equipped with a general all-purpose three-blade propeller. If the motor is applied to an exceptionally heavy boat, or one which is exceptionally heavily loaded, the motor may be able to peak out at only 4,200 r.p.m. At this speed, the motor is developing far less than its rated horsepower. The owner who operates his boat in this condition might better have saved himself money by purchasing a 35-horsepower motor, for his 40-horsepower motor at only 4,200 r.p.m. just won't produce the full-rated output. Since he wanted 40 horsepower, he must make the necessary modifications to his equipment setup—that is propeller, engine angle, or transom height—to get what he initially wanted and paid for.

Only with a tachometer is it possible for the boat owner to be assured that his motor can reach its full-rated r.p.m. and hence full-rated horsepower. It is possible, however, to develop full-rated horsepower, that is, permit the motor to wind out to its rated peak, with varying combinations of propellers and setups. Yet without the water speedometer as a complementary instrument, the owner has no means of knowing which of the various setups offers the most efficient choice, i.e. full-rated horsepower with maximum speed.

Though few outboard motor owners are aware of it, all outboard motors—for that matter, all internal combustion engines—develop less horsepower and efficiency as operating altitude increases. A motor running at sea level has more output than that same motor pushing an identical load on a mountain lake. A similar loss in horsepower occurs as weather conditions vary from cool to extremely hot, muggy, midsummer temperatures. By use of a water speedometer and tachometer, this horsepower loss can be measured and adjustments made to compensate for it, so that at least a part of the lost performance can be recovered. The way to do this is covered partially in the discussion of carburetion, Chapter 4, and partially in the section on propellers, Chapter 12.

11. Engine Angle and Transom Height

Any knowing boatman can look over a group of twenty or thirty boats on any busy waterway and observe that 50 per cent of them are handling poorly. Some will mush, some porpoise, but only a few of them will ride as a well-designed boat should. This poor performance usually is due not to poor boat design, nor to a mismatching of motor and boat, but rather to improper setup of the motor on the boat.

The modern outboard hull, whether it's a runabout, utility, day cruiser, or cruiser, is designed as a semiplaning hull. It is intended to run on the surface of the water, rather than through the water. Because of its modest size fore and aft and athwartships, balance is critical. Motor adjustments can be made to counteract poor balance.

Unfortunately, an inconsistency exists in both motor and boat designs as concerns suitable transom heights. Some manufacturers have built their standard unit motors to operate with greatest degree of efficiency set up on a transom 15″ to 16″ high. Other manufacturer's motors, in standard lower unit format, perform more efficiently at transom heights of 16″ to 17″. The variance of two inches may seem small and you may think its effect on performance would be negligible. Yet drivers of outboard racing equipment have found that variations in height as little as $\frac{1}{32}$″ may result in very appreciable speed gain or loss. Though pleasure boat performance is not so critical, variations of $\frac{1}{4}$″ in transom height can be measured easily in terms of appreciable gains or losses in speed.

This has long placed the boatbuilder in a quandary, for he has no way of foretelling what brand of motor, with its individual requirement for a certain transom height, will be used on his boat. Though most manufacturers' long-unit driveshaft housings are 5″ longer than the short housings, boat transom heights of deep transom hulls may also vary from 20″ to 21″ or even 22″.

Added to these differences in transom heights are variations in the bottom design of hulls and angles of the transoms. A hull with a perfectly flat bottom or a modest degree of V-ing or dead rise may permit a higher on-the-transom mounting for most satisfactory performance, while a boat of similar weight, length, and width with a deeper keel may call for a shallower mounting in order for the propeller to operate in water which is freer from keel turbulence.

One word which becomes important to any outboarder is cavitation. Cavitation is that situation in which a propeller rotates inefficiently with little thrust due to an inability of the propeller's blades to bite in solid water. This situation occurs when a propeller is operating near the surface in less dense water, or in disturbed water caused by the forward motion of the hull, or in air pockets in the water. Some boats that perform without cavitation or excessive propeller slippage on the straightaway may cavitate badly in turns. Cavitation on the straightaway may be corrected by changing the motor mounting height to bury the propeller deeper in the water.

Some round chine boats bank excessively in turns so that it is nearly impossible to adjust the motor height for peak performance on the straightaway and still prevent propeller slip-

Inspection of your outboard motor will show the means to alter motor-transom angle. Note here, several inches above water line on clamp bracket, four notches for changing position of this motor.

page in tight turns. The owner of such a boat, for pleasure use, should set his motor at a depth just below the point of cavitation on the straightaway. In turns, he should reduce motor speed, increase his turning radius, or both.

Perfect motor height for any given propeller may be arrived at only with the use of the water speedometer. Peak reading at full throttle will indicate when the correct height is reached. Cavitation will result in a measurable reduction of speed. However, a reasonably accurate motor height adjustment may be made by ear, and it is done in the following way:

The motor is first mounted on the transom at the cutout height provided by the boat's manufacturer. The boat is run at full throttle, and the operator must listen carefully to hear whether or not the motor seems to be breaking free, that is winding excessively without any noticeable increase in speed or a loss in speed. If no slippage is noted, that is, an intermittent or continuous over-revving of the engine with excessive tur-

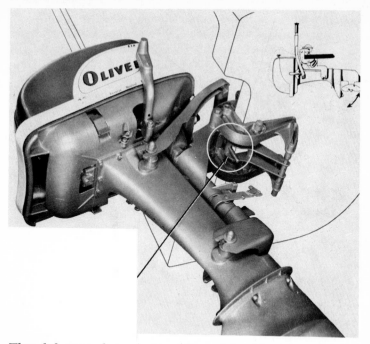

Threaded screw shown in insert is used by this motor manufacturer to permit an infinite number of tilt positions for maximum performance.

bulence of the propeller and a consequent reduction in boat speed (comparable to an automobile's wheels spinning on glare ice, snow, or sand without efficient forward motion), the boat owner should continue to increase the motor height in lesser and lesser increments until the point of cavitation is reached.

Shim sticks are used for this purpose. Sections of a ruler or yardstick or strips of plywood will suffice. When the point of cavitation is reached, the owner should drop the motor again about 1/4″, repeat his underway run, and, if no cavitation is noted, a suitable transom height has been arrived at.

Keep in mind that the motor clamp brackets must be firmly clamped to the solid transom, not on the shims. Do not increase transom height with shims to such a point that the clamps no longer can firmly bite into the transom proper. Should such a radical increase in height be called for, you should add a permanently screwed shim section.

Many of the larger motors call for bolting of the motor's clamp brackets to the transom in addition to clamping. Your operational manual will indicate if this is recommended for your motor, and if so, by all means bolt the motor to the transom once you have adjusted and attained the proper height setting.

Every outboard motor manufacturer has provided some means to alter the engine angle. An inspection of your own bracket will indicate how this is done, by adjustment notches or variation of metal dowel pin in bracket holes. Motors with remote gearshifts usually will require the motor to be shifted into a forward position, for most motors are so designed that they will not tilt up in neutral or reverse. Be certain your ignition switch is off before making any motor mount alterations or propeller changes.

For your initial setup of boat-motor angle, once your motor has been placed on the transom, place some form of straight edge along the boat's bottom extending aft and adjust the motor so that the anticavitation plate is closely parallel to the straight edge. The anticavitation plate is the broad, flat, finlike section horizontal to the water's surface above the propeller gear housing. Most boats operate best when the cavitation plate is parallel or when the plate slants slightly upward at its trailing edge from a parallel plane to the boat's after-planing surface.

If after you have set the motor angle, your boat tends to porpoise (that is, the bow rises and falls rhythmically with a spanking motion), it will be necessary for you to bring the motor in toward the transom one adjustment, reducing the angle between transom and drive-shaft housing.

If, however, the boat buries its bow and the forward section of the boat does not ride free of the water, the motor angle must be increased by adjusting the tilt of the motor outward.

You may have noted that when underway and a passenger moved from the front seat to the rear of the boat, the boat gained in speed, or vice versa. This is a matter of boat balance. In effect, the shift in passenger weight served to alter the angle of attack or thrust of the propeller, in much the same manner that would occur if the motor had been brought out so that the drive shaft formed a larger angle with the transom. Weight shifts in small boats can be accomplished underway, while shifts of motor angle call for stopping the boat. If your

This boat operator illustrates how shim sticks may be added to transom to increase transom height and decrease depth that motor's lower unit operates under water.

boat is a bit flighty under choppy water conditions, and tends to porpoise, a shift of passenger or gear load forward usually will correct this. Movable weight such as remote fuel tanks may be used, though I favor properly balancing the boat with motor adjustments.

You may find that your boat when properly set for operation on smooth water has a tendency to cavitate or may become wild in its handling characteristics on rough water. If this occurs, it is a simple matter to bring the motor in toward the transom slightly, which will tend to level off the boat and smooth out the ride.

Proper maintenance is an important factor in good boat performance. The boat owner who continually trails his boat to and from launching sites and stores his boat on a trailer with motor installed should be careful to see that the hull is given proper support. For example, if the boat is transported on a trailer that is too short, so that a half foot or more of the stern of the boat has no support, the weight of the engine can create a hook in the bottom—that is, a concavity will be formed forward of the transom. This usually will result in the boat plowing or riding bow heavy. The boat's performance will probably be reduced, since the boatbuilder's original bottom design has been altered through carelessness.

Some boat owners make a practice of storing heavy camping gear in their boats, or allowing water to collect in the bilges. This may cause the boat to sag and take on a rocker-type design. A boat with a rocker will probably ride bow high. Motor angle adjustments will compensate somewhat for changes in the planing surface brought about through carelessness.

Finally the boat owner may find that his boat, which reached plane readily with several passengers, has difficulty in reaching and maintaining plane under heavy load or when pulling water skiers. A propeller change obviously is called for, but some of the lost performance can be regained, if no substitute propeller is available, by bringing the propeller in closer to the transom of the boat, reducing the transom angle.

If you notice that your motor with the same setup has suddenly taken on a tendency to cavitate or speed has fallen off appreciably, it's probable that this has been caused by an accumulation of marine growth, which is creating turbulence not present when the boat bottom was clean. This, of course, can be corrected only by pulling the boat from the water and removing the growth.

12. Propeller Selection and Care

You may own a beautifully designed boat, have it mated with the perfect motor for the size and weight of the boat, and yet without a proper propeller, performance can be mediocre or even downright disappointing.

Many small boatmen have clung to the theory that a propeller advances a boat through the water in much the manner that a screw progresses through a solid. Propellers even have been referred to as screws, and this misconception concerning the manner in which a propeller functions has increased.

The screw theory very probably came into being because of the means used to describe the function of one of the propeller's two dimensions. A propeller ordinarily is marked in diameter and pitch. Diameter is readily measured and doesn't confuse boatmen. On a two-bladed propeller, it is the distance measured from the extremes of either blade tip. On a three-bladed propeller, the diameter is measured by doubling the distance from the center of the propeller hub to the extreme end of any of the three blade tips. Thus you can see that diameter is actually the diameter of the circle that the propeller blade makes as it rotates.

Pitch is a more confusing factor, and the pitch of a propeller frequently has been compared to the thread of a screw. The blades of a boat's propeller are not on a flat plane: one blade edge leads the other edge. In explaining the function of pitch, the example is often given that if the propeller were rotated one complete revolution through a semisolid, such as putty, and in one complete revolution the propeller were to advance 10″, the propeller would be referred to as one with a 10″ pitch. This attributes a screw motion to a propeller.

If you know the circumference of an automobile wheel and the number of revolutions per minute that the rear axles on an automobile rotate, by simple mathematics, you can determine how many feet per minute the car will advance by multiplying r.p.m. of the car's axle by the circumference of the automobile wheel in feet.

Boat propellers are given pitch ratings in terms of inches. If there were no slippage, one could figure the number of inches a boat would advance per minute by merely multiplying the pitch of the propeller by the number of r.p.m. the propeller shaft is rotating. However, no propeller on a boat operates at 100 per cent or even close to 100 per cent efficiency. And to destroy such an analogy further, a boat's propeller does not perform as a screw. Instead, a boat is propelled by the thrust of accelerated water against motionless or nearly motionless water. You could propel your boat with a garden hose or a fire hose merely by training one with sufficient pressure from the rear of the boat. The thrust of the accelerated water would push the boat forward.

A propeller, in rotating, draws water through it much in the manner that a fan draws air from one side of the fan's blades and exhausts it through the other.

Diameter and a third factor in wheel design, blade area, have a part in imparting motion to a boat. As it rotates, the propeller

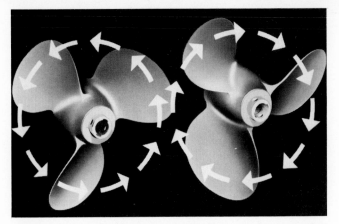

Arrows indicate direction of propeller rotation, showing how leading edge of each blade is positioned closer to gearbox of lower unit than trailing edge. Some manufacturers provide counter-rotating crankshafts and prop shafts for twin installations. (Courtesy, Oliver Motors)

or wheel draws water through its leading edge and expels it from the trailing edges of the blades in a spiral movement. The propeller blades actually are thrusting constantly. And this propeller thrust is used to advance the boat.

The amount of the propeller thrust does not depend on pitch alone, but rather on a combination of the speed of rotation of the propeller (which is a product of the horsepower of the motor and the combined pitch), and the area and diameter of a given propeller. Remember that work accomplished is horsepower. The horsepower of your outboard motor is a product of the r.p.m. of the crankshaft. As we have pointed out earlier, each outboard motor is rated at a maximum horsepower at a specific r.p.m. If the motor does not reach this r.p.m., it cannot develop its full-rated horsepower. As a result, when you select a propeller, you can only find the best one for any boat and motor combination by means of the two instruments I have described: water speedometer and tachometer.

The manufacturer of your motor may well have equipped its prop shaft with what he considered an average propeller for that particular power plant. This propeller selection is only a studied guess on the part of the manufacturer. Market report data can offer him information on the type boat, size, and pas-

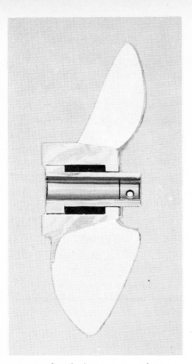

Most present-day motors feature propellers with some form of rubber shock absorber in propeller hub. Dark section here is the rubber mounting. (Courtesy, Johnson Motors)

senger load the average boat operator will apply to his motor. But your boat may be heavier or lighter by far than this average craft.

To offset this disadvantage, there is a gradually growing tendency for the manufacturers to leave propeller selection to the dealer or the consumer. The motor manufacturer has come to realize that this average wheel will prove to be the best wheel only in a few instances. At one time when outboard motors were applied to small utilities, and the boats were expected to offer only low-speed performance for fishing or general pleasure boating activities, the average wheel could do the job.

However, when large horsepower motors are applied to a variety of hull designs, ranging from lightweight sports runabouts and utilities, large day cruisers or cruisers, and each boat is expected to perform a variety of jobs, the average propeller can't be expected to give more than a mediocre performance. If you expect to use your boat for general pleasure boating, water skiing, or weekend camping junkets, you will need two and perhaps even three different propellers to gain the best efficiency from your outfit at all times.

Propeller thrust, as mentioned earlier, can be measured in terms of pounds. Both motor and propeller manufacturers have all conducted extensive tests using varying means to determine propeller thrust. To offer an idea of the difference in static thrust in pounds between propellers of varying pitch, diameter, and number of blades recorded on an individual motor, one 40-horsepower outboard engine with which I conducted prop tests was fitted with a three-blade 10″ diameter, 11″ pitch wheel. At full throttle, this propeller produced a scale recording of 495 pounds. A two-bladed 10″ by 16″ wheel indicated a thrust of 330 pounds. A 45-horsepower motor with a 10½″ diameter, 11″ pitch, three-blade wheel at full throttle had a static thrust of 465 pounds, while a two-blade wheel of 10½″ diameter and 15″ pitch showed 385 pounds thrust.

These were static thrust tests with engines mounted on swiveling mounting pads, tugging via a cable on a scale. None of the propellers could be considered right or wrong for the engine since the only work accomplished was thrust against a scale for test purposes. The test is mentioned, however, to show the considerable difference that changes in diameter and pitch can produce.

For the boatman, the important feature in propeller selection is not the static thrust but the performance of the propeller of a given boat under particular load conditions in terms of acceleration and speed.

A tachometer used in conjunction with the water speedometer will give this answer. The boat owner should remember that first he wants to select a propeller or several propellers that for his particular operations will permit his motor to develop its full-rated horsepower. If your motor gains its

Damaged or bent propellers may be repaired by most dealers who carry a set of pitch blocks such as this one. Damaged propeller is carefully hammered back into shape to match contours of propeller mandril.

The Multi-Pitch propeller, available for many current models of outboard motors, combines within one propeller a large number of different pitches for operation under varying conditions.

horsepower rating at 4,500 r.p.m., for example, refer to your tachometer when selecting a propeller and be sure that at full throttle, the motor reaches this maximum r.p.m. Be equally certain that the propeller does not allow the motor materially to exceed this figure, for your horsepower developed may be less at higher as well as lower r.p.m., and excess r.p.m. may do damage to the motor.

Conceivably a number of different propellers will offer this recommended peak r.p.m. engine performance. Next you must choose the propeller which offers the maximum speed at that full-rated r.p.m. in order to attain the greatest potential efficiency inherent to motor and boat design. This is where the

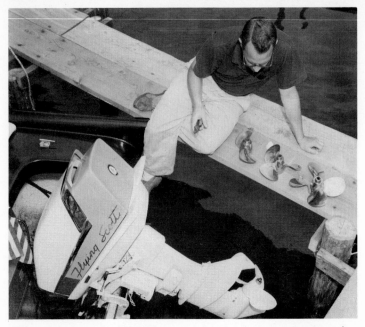

This motor is equipped with manufacturer's "average operating condition" propeller. Owner on dock has a selection of three additional propellers designed for this motor to offer greatest efficiency at varying loads and operating conditions.

water speedometer comes into use. The tachometer indicates the propellers that offer full horsepower—the water speedometer tells which of those propellers is the most efficient for use on your boat for a specific application. And remember, the propeller that is right for water ski towing will not be the most efficient for some other form of activity.

There are a number of guides in propeller selection. On a light boat, you usually will find that greatest speed is attained from a two-blade propeller of high pitch rather than from a three-bladed propeller of lesser pitch.

For water skiing or hauling heavy passenger loads, you will require greater propeller thrust, which you may expect to gain from a three-bladed propeller. However, with heavy loads, you will find that you will have to resort to a lower pitch wheel in order for the motor to reach its maximum-rated r.p.m.

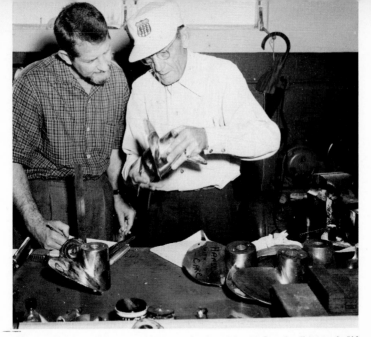

The author, at left, makes notes during his study of effects of different propellers on prop thrust of a variety of motors.

So, in general, you will need a low-pitch propeller for heavy loads, a high-pitch, two-blade for light loads, and a propeller of a pitch between the two for average pleasure boating conditions.

As the angle of attack of the blade increases (that is the blades are twisted so as to become less and less close to parallel to the direction of arc of rotation of the propeller), pitch is increased. As the blades gradually are flattened and approach closer and closer to a flat disc, pitch is decreased or lowered. So in terms of number designations, a 15″ pitch propeller has a higher pitch, calls for more power to rotate it than does, for example, a lesser pitch 10″ wheel of the same diameter and blade area.

Pitch generally may be expected to be increased as the work load is decreased. The pitch is increased in order to hold down maximum r.p.m. within safety limits. The reverse holds true as the load is increased.

To the racing driver, of course, propeller choice is even more important than it is to the pleasure boatman. The racing driver is interested in even such fine speed increments as small fractions of a mile per hour, which might be gained by more careful balancing of the propeller, cupping of the blades to get greater bite, or other minute variations. Cupping of propeller blades, a commonplace practice of the racing fraternity, effects an increase in pitch at the blade tips only. Sometimes this will be done to offset cavitation or to give greater acceleration out of the turns. For the pleasure boatmen, propellers unaltered from manufacturer's designs will suffice.

The maintenance of propellers is equally as important to the boat's performance as initial selection. From time to time, all pleasure boatmen will experience the misfortune of having their motor's propeller strike against the bottom or clobber a piece of floating debris. Sometimes no visually noticeable damage is done but the astute boatman may detect the sudden development of motor and boat vibrations not evident prior to striking the propeller. He may notice, too, a sudden measurable decrease in maximum speed. What probably has occurred is that one of the blades has been bent, yet, since it is not nicked, the bending of the blade was not apparent. Still the bent blade has altered pitch, and performance has been impaired.

For the author's tests, different motors were mounted on this swiveling boom which could be raised or lowered to simulate varying transom heights. Control of motor was at a remote location. Motor pulled against a Dillon spring scale.

The boatman who does notice this would be wise to take the propeller to a dealer and have the blades checked. Most dealers have pitch blocks and pitch testing equipment so they can determine whether or not the propeller has been damaged and, if it has, whether or not it can be returned to its original factory configuration.

Propeller blades that are badly nicked can cause vibrations that will lead to rapid wear of lower unit gears, bushings, bearings, or even set up damaging vibrations in the rotating and reciprocating parts of the powerhead. Propellers are relatively inexpensive items when contrasted to the over-all investment in a complete motor. Any boat operator would be wise to see that his motor's propellers are kept in perfect condition to protect the major investment that turns the propeller.

Pitting and corrosion of the propeller blades can cause a loss in propeller efficiency. For this reason, those who operate their boats in salt water should take particular pains to see that the motor's lower end is tilted out of water at the completion of each period of operation. The propeller should be flushed with fresh water and then given a light protective coating of lower unit lubricant.

Many motors still have shearable pins installed by the builder so that when the propeller strikes a solid object, the

Operational panel location for static prop thrust tests included remote controls for varying types of motors plus tachometer and electrical starting wiring harness.

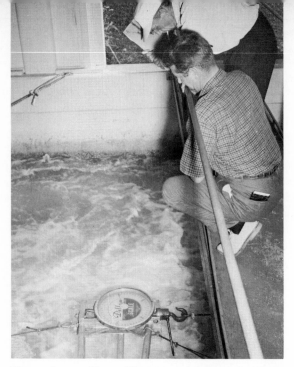

The author studies pulling power of motor in operation as recorded on Dillon scale. Various propeller sizes offered a broad range of results.

pin rather than other internal motor parts receives the shock load. The sheared pin relieves the drive train of strain so that the shock is not reflected beyond the shearable pin location. When replacing shear pins, boat operators should use extreme caution. A warm outboard motor can restart easily with the slightest twist of the flywheel. When grasping the propeller and rotating it, you are performing a turn of the flywheel, and a spark may be produced, setting the propeller into action.

If your motor is an electric-starting type, be certain that the key is turned to an "off" position. Warn any passengers not to touch the key while you are pulling the propeller. If you have no positive means to be sure that the motor cannot accidentally start, remove the motor's cowling and disconnect the plug lead wires. This simple precaution can save you from being seriously cut by whirling propeller blades.

Whenever a propeller is pulled, always coat the propeller shaft with a film of waterproof grease so that corrosion will not make it difficult to remove the propeller at another time.

Many manufacturers today are equipping their motors with rubber-cushioned propeller hubs. Some of these are a substitute for the shear pin and are so designed that when a propeller strikes an object, the internal parts of the hub slip so as to preclude any damage to other parts of the engine.

Other manufacturers use the rubber hub in conjunction with some form of shear or drive pin. However, the rubber hub usually will take the shock so that the annoyance of replacing shear pins is a rarity.

When selecting a replacement propeller, however, if the original propeller was fitted with a rubber insert, you would be wise to buy only a replacement with a shock absorber insert, or your motor may be damaged. This is particularly true if the replacement propeller is a heavy bronze one and the factory original was aluminum.

With a heavy bronze replacement, in certain instances you may find that suddenly you are plagued with having to replace shear pins frequently. This has occurred because the heavier propeller has greater inertia. As you accelerate rapidly, this greater inertia results in shear-pin breakage, or, if your motor is not fitted with shear pins, it can damage lower unit gears, prop shaft, drive shaft, or crankshaft.

Recently a manufacturer introduced a reasonably priced, variable pitch propeller. This variable pitch propeller is designed to fit many of the motors currently on the market. Unquestionably, year by year, additional variable pitch propellers of differing designs will be made so that they can be applied to motors of nearly any manufacture. The design permits a mechanical change of pitch so that a single variable pitch propeller will offer a choice suitable for efficient operation under varying conditions of boat load.

You may wonder whether or not such propellers are efficient or merely gimmicks of no value. I have conducted rather extensive tests of the Multi-Pitch propeller, a design offering a range of seven pitches in a single propeller. I find that the Multi-Pitch is efficient, offers performance equal to or only slightly less than fixed-pitch propellers of any of the comparable sizes offered within a Multi-Pitch range. Because of this I feel that the Multi-Pitch wheels can be recommended for any model motor for which they are designed, and effect an economy and convenience. The current Multi-Pitch propellers in general give the range of propeller selection necessary for all boat applications, except for the owner of an extremely light boat hoping to reach competition speeds.

The Multi-Pitch propeller blades, like those of any fixed-pitch type, can be broken, but replacement blades are available at low cost (far less than the amount to replace a fixed-pitch blade), and the hub mechanism is sufficiently rugged so that the possibility of damage to it is remote even under the most destructive conditions.

13. The Dunked Motor

It is no rarity for an outboard motor to be dunked. Of course, competition boats overturn frequently, but I even know of one case of a red-faced racing driver who dropped his motor overboard while trying to put it on the transom.

Pleasure boat motors also come in for their share of duckings. On a number of occasions I have seen owners trailer-launch their boat and motor and subject the motor to a real shower bath. In one instance, the owner forgot to install the drain plugs. The boat and motor swished off the trailer in a slickly greased roller-type motion. With neither bow nor mooring line attached, the boat surged out twenty yards from the beach and slowly gurgled to the bottom.

Boats have upset and been swamped at their moorings or filled with rain and finally capsized. I once had my boat neatly tethered to a tree overhanging a small inland channel on the west coast of Florida near the Gulf of Mexico. I left in company with other boatmen, returned after the tide had dropped much farther than I anticipated and had come back in again over the transom of my boat which was hanging stern down on a too-short tether. My boat was upside down, and the motor had been submerged for an hour or more.

A water-sodden motor can be your misfortune, too. What to do about it is important.

The first aid required is relatively simple if the motor was not operating when it went overboard. But prompt action

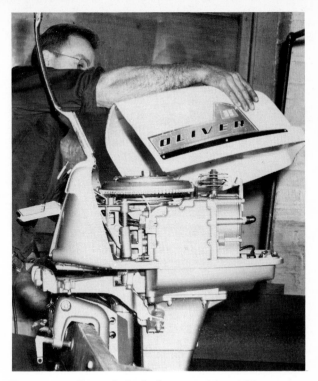

Remove cowling of dunked motor as quickly as possible after motor has been retrieved.

should be taken the moment the motor is removed from the water. As long as the motor is submerged, rust and corrosion will be an extremely slow process. Motors have been hauled off the bottom, even in salt water, after several weeks and have appeared to be almost new. But the moment the motor is exposed to air, rust and corrosion will start, and you must take immediate steps to prevent their damaging action.

Even an overnight delay after a motor has been retrieved from under water can cause sufficient damage so that an entire new set of internal bearings will be required.

The first thing to do is to rid the power plant of as much water as possible. Place it upright on a motor stand, the back of a bench, a weighted folding chair, or a boat's transom, then remove the cowling. Disconnect spark plug leads and remove the spark plugs so that water will drain from the spark plug

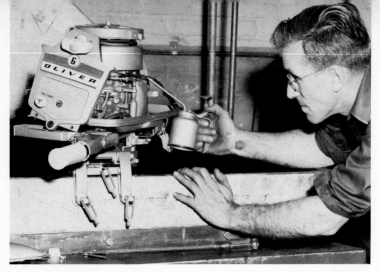

Spray ignition system with carbon tetrachloride to remove moisture.

holes. If your motor is fitted with air intake silencers over the carburetor, remove the silencer or silencers to expose the throats of the carburetors.

With the ready-pull starter, rotate the motor to see if it is free. If it is free, tilt the motor backward and pour a generous supply of gasoline-oil mixture into the carburetor. Then pull the flywheel over so that the gasoline-oil mixture thoroughly circulates through all the powerhead's rotating and reciprocating parts and is expelled through the spark plug holes.

The fuel purging will flush out the water remaining in the crankcase and piston assembly as well as in the fuel intake and exhaust passages. Operate the flywheel slowly at first and then more vigorously as the flushing procedure proceeds. Water will not only be flushed away but the motor's working parts will be bathed with a protective coat of oil.

CAUTION: Keep in mind that the fumes from the gasoline-oil mixture are highly flammable. Perform this flushing process out of doors. Have a fire extinguisher handy in the event your precautions against fire are not successful. Remember that your ignition system can still produce sparks, so ground each of the high-tension leads against the metal of the powerhead.

When you feel you have thoroughly flushed the engine, you should drain all fuel from the fuel system, since it may have become water contaminated. Remove the carburetor

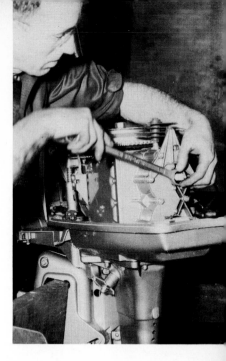

Remove spark plugs.

filter bowl, let the lines drain, and as a final precaution, blow through the fuel leads. Flush the filter bowl with fresh gasoline and dry it. Then replace the carburetor air filter and fuel lines. Check the spark plugs to see if any water remains on the plugs. If so, these, too, should be washed. Use clear gasoline or carbon tetrachloride and allow the plugs to dry.

Replace the spark plugs. Hang the motor in a test tank or replace it on the boat's transom. Try it out with your normal starting procedure. If it runs, permit it to idle for three or four minutes. Then you will be safe to store it, for the oil in your fuel mixture will by that time have had an opportunity to form a film over all the motor's internal parts.

Do not run the motor out of water. Water must circulate through the cooling system because overheating can cause as much damage as rust.

You may find that the ignition system was shorted by the soaking or some of the ignition components may have been damaged by water. The components, however, of a modern outboard motor are sealed against dampness and usually will survive a dunking.

Remove carburetor air silencer. Drain all water possible from engine, then pour fuel-oil mixture through throat of carburetor as engine is rotated.

However, if you have no spark, and even if you have, this suggestion will prove to be a good precaution. You should expose the ignition system and spray the entire contents with carbon tetrachloride. An automobile-type fire extinguisher about the size of a beer can will take care of this, and you'll find it's a matter of only a few minutes before the entire ignition system is bone dry.

If you do not have access to carbon tetrachloride, then leave the magneto exposed to the sun. Do not be tempted to remove the magneto and bake it in an oven. Baking at an excessive temperature can cause extensive damage to ignition system components by melting sealing compounds designed to waterproof components or by cooking away the insulation.

Disconnect all fuel lines, drain carburetor filter bowl, flush carburetor gas tank, and reassemble.

Wash spark plugs in clean gasoline or (preferably) an acetone bath.

Use air hose to blow spark plugs dry.

The ignition system of some outboard motors is difficult to get at. If you cannot expose yours so that it can be dried easily, better get the motor to a dealer just as quickly as possible so it can be checked by an experienced repairman. Outboard repair shops will have complete ignition equipment so each component can be checked and any faulty ones replaced.

One of the most important things to remember is that during the period of submersion, sand, silt and other contaminations may have worked their way into your remote fuel tank or integral fuel tank. The fuel tank and the entire line must be carefully flushed. A few tiny grains of sand introduced into the piston assembly can score the pistons and piston rings, leading to a compression loss that will measurably reduce horsepower.

If your motor, however, was running at high speed and was thrown from the boat's transom in an abrupt turn, or your boat flipped and the motor was submerged while running, unless you were extremely fortunate, internal damage may have occurred. Water does not compress. If a considerable amount of

Care taken in handling of motors when mounting or removing from a boat will minimize any chance of a dunked motor.

water entered the cylinders either through the fuel intake or the exhaust passages, the moving piston, in thrusting outward toward the end of the cylinder, would have encountered this noncompressible mass. Damage to wrist pins, connecting rods, or crankshaft is likely to have occurred. At slow speed, however, the engine very probably would have merely stalled and drowned out.

If, after retrieving the motor and draining the water as described previously, you note *any* feeling of dragging or resistance to the pull of the starter cord, your wisest move would be to have your local dealer tear down the motor entirely and check all components for damage.

A motor which has rested for some period of time on a soft

Cowboy antics like this can lead to an upset and may mean costly repairs.

Sitting on gunwales leads to swamping and upsets.

bottom may have taken in considerable sand, grit, silt, or mud into the motor's innards. Another potential type of damage would be the clogging of the motor's cooling system. After any submersion in a soft bottom, be certain to flush the engine's cooling system. Mud caking in the cooling passages can prevent a free flow of coolant, and overheating can lead to scoring or even seizure of internal parts.

Any dunking can prove troublesome and may be expensive. Care in properly securing the motor to the boat's transom, a routine check of automatic drain plugs prior to launching, care in launching and retrieving—as well as in mooring—and a resistance to cowboying tactics on the water will eliminate most things leading to need for artificial respiration of your powerhead.

14. Off-Season Storage

Proper off-season storage methods will preserve your motor in the same condition it was in at the time you put it away.

The first step in preparing for storage is to see that all water is drained from the motor's cooling system. Place the motor on a motor stand or a similarly convenient rack and, with spark plug leads disconnected, rotate with the hand starter so that the water remaining in the coolant passages is drained.

Keep in mind, however, that with some makes of motors, it is impossible to drain all the water from the coolant passages of the cylinder block assembly. If you live in an area where there is any chance of freezing, store the motor in a heated location.

Check the lower unit and refill it with the prescribed lubricant. Rotate the motor again several times so that a protective film covers gears and bearing surfaces.

Your motor will have a protection of oil film from its last operation. However, it is recommended that at least once a month during the winter you rotate the motor several times by hand so that there is no opportunity for gum formations to cause parts of the engine to seize to one another.

Remove the cowling of the motor before storage and spray the internal components with a rust-preventive film. Your marine dealer will carry a rust preventive in a handy pressur-

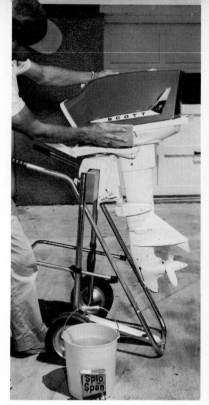

Prior to storing motor during off season, wash it down with a good detergent. If it is not marred or scratched, then give it a coat of hard car wax or wipe it with an oily cloth to protect it.

ized spray can. Clean all exposed surfaces of the engine and retouch nicks and abrasions at the time of storage rather than waiting for the following spring.

The storage period, too, is the time to check over the motor thoroughly, tightening all securing hardware and inspecting such items as high-tension leads of the ignition system, flexible fuel lines, and other parts subject to wear. Replace these as necessary.

Many outboard dealers make a specialty during the off-season months of storing outboard motors. In the price of storage, they include a complete inspection of the motor, charging only for necessary parts and labor required to keep the motor in first-class operating condition. If your local dealer offers such service, you may prefer this to taking on the storage preparations yourself.

Spray-coat any nicks to prevent further deterioration. Your dealer carries pressurized cans of paint in colors to match those used on your motor.

Electric-starting motors require little more storage attention than do the manual-starting types. If you are storing your boat in the open, however, it is recommended that you remove the electrical wiring junction box and give this a dry storage location. Spray or coat ignition switch controls, or preferably remove these, too, and store in a dry location.

Your battery should not be permitted to run down. It will be subject to less discharge if stored in a cool area. But keep in mind that the electrolyte of a discharged battery can freeze. The freezing of a battery will ruin it. Cool storage does not infer freezing temperature.

Store your battery indoors, protect it from dampness, and, about every two to three weeks, take a hydrometer reading. Batteries with less than one-half charge should be recharged for their protection. Never permit a fast charge of your outboard battery as this will lead to its rapid deterioration, but do not allow it to discharge beyond the half-charge point.

In recent years many dealers have initiated a service to provide electric-starting battery storage and will place your bat-

Don't be tempted to save fuel from one season to the next. Varnish and other residues form in gasoline when it is stored over long periods.

tery on slow charge whenever it is required, so that the following season it will be in perfect condition.

The cost of this service is only a fraction of the cost of a new battery.

Do not economize by trying to save unused outboard fuel from one season to the next. Empty your outboard tank at the end of the season, and flush it with clear gasoline, for residual oil may form gum and tar over the winter months. Store the tank in a dry protected area with the filler cap removed or the filler cap vent open.

Do not cover either your outboard motor, battery, or fuel tank with an airtight cover; condensation may occur under such a cover, leading to damage and rust caused by dampness. A loose cover under which the air can circulate but which will keep the dust away is recommended.

Check over ignition, tighten all loose hardware, drain and clean
filter bowl, lubricate moving parts, then cover motor with some
form of dust protection. Original shipping carton affords ideal
storage.

SAFETY FIRST

The Golden Rule for boat handling is "Safety First and Keep to the Right."

Time should never be considered wasted if safety is at stake.

Rules of the road are applicable to all boats when underway and a boat is considered underway when she is not at anchor, aground, or made fast to the shore.

A power boat gives way to a sail boat except when being overtaken.

Power boats meeting head-on pass portside to portside, unless signaled otherwise.

Any vessel being overtaken by another has the right of way.

Any vessel having right of way shall hold her course and speed, unless such action would cause a collision.

The danger zone is from dead ahead to two points abaft the starboard beam.

Any power boat having another in its danger zone shall give way to the other and shall, if necessary, alter course, slacken speed, stop, or reverse.

A vessel (under 65 feet) using both sail and power acts as a power boat by day but as a sail boat by night.

A sail boat running free gives way to the one close hauled.

A sail boat running free with the wind on the port gives way to one running free with the wind on the starboard.

When two sail boats are running alike, the one to the windward gives way.

WHISTLE SIGNALS FOR POWER BOATS

A vessel's right cannot be altered by whistle signals; the one which whistles first gains no rights over another; cross signals are unlawful.

If the signal is correct for the circumstances, answer it; if it is not, give the danger signal, stop, and come to an understanding.

1 Short Blast—I wish to leave you on my port.

2 Short Blasts—I wish to leave you on my starboard.

3 Short Blasts—My engines are going astern; I am doing my best to stop.

4 Short Blasts—Danger, stop, your signals are not clear or are not satisfactory to me.

Whistle signals are never given to or'by a sail boat.

Every whistle signal should be answered with a like signal if the maneuver indicated is safe.

FOG SIGNALS FOR POWER BOATS

1 Long Blast—I am under way.

1 Long and 2 Short Blasts—I am towing something.

FOG HORN SIGNALS FOR SAIL BOATS

1 Short Blast—I am on the starboard tack.

2 Short Blasts—I am on the port tack.

3 Short Blasts—I am running free.

1 Long and 2 Short Blasts—I am being towed (any vessel).

Rapid bell—I am at anchor (any vessel).

Any boatman operating commercially or for pleasure who adheres to the above rules and who answers whistle signals properly marks himself as a seaman and a gentleman.

—Courtesy, *Inland Waterway Guide*